MEDIAEVAL CASTLES
IN NORTH WALES

A STUDY OF SITES, WATER SUPPLY
AND BUILDING STONES

By

E. NEAVERSON, D.Sc., F.G.S.

THE UNIVERSITY PRESS OF LIVERPOOL
HODDER AND STOUGHTON LTD., LONDON
1947

A TRIBUTE TO
THE MEMORY OF
W. L. HOBBS
(1868 - 1947)

C. Tinling & Co., Ltd., Printers, Liverpool, London & Prescot

CONTENTS

PAGE

INTRODUCTION V

CHAPTER

I GEOLOGICAL FEATURES OF THE CHESHIRE
BORDERLAND 1

II GENERAL GEOLOGICAL FEATURES OF NORTH WALES 6

III CASTLE MOUNDS WITHOUT BUILDINGS . . . 17

IV THE EARLY ENGLISH STONE CASTLES . . 22

V THE WELSH STONE CASTLES 31

VI THE CASTLES OF EDWARD I 40

APPENDIX: REFERENCES TO LITERATURE CITED IN THE
TEXT 52

INDEX 54

ILLUSTRATIONS

FIG.   PAGE

1. Geological sketch-map of Chester . . . 2
2. Geological sketch-map of Beeston Castle . . 4
3. Geology and location of Castles in North Wales . 7
4. Diagram-section to show the chief sandstones in the Carboniferous system of North Wales . . 9
5. Vale of Edeyrnion ; geology and mounds . . 20
6. Geological sketch-map of Hawarden Castle . . 26
7. Tomen y Mur, view from the South . . *facing* 27
8. Denbigh Castle, view from the West . . *facing* 27
9. Geological sketch-map of country around Caergwrle Castle 27
10. Denbigh Castle and Walled Town, geological sketch-map 29
11. Dolwyddelan Castle, geological sketch-map . . 32
12. Ewloe Castle, geological sketch-map . . . 35
13. Dolbadarn Castle, view from the north-west *facing* 35
14. Deganwy Castle, view of site from the western bank of the Conway estuary . . . . *facing* 35
15. Castell Dinas Bran, view from the East . *facing* 37
16. Criccieth Castle, view from the East . . *facing* 37
17. Rhuddlan Castle, view from the north-west *facing* 43
18. Harlech Castle, view from the North . . *facing* 43
19. Conway Castle and Town Walls, geological sketch-map 44
20. Caernarvon Castle and Walled Town, geological sketch-map 46
21. Dolwyddelan Castle, doorway in West Tower *facing* 50
22. Beaumaris Castle, doorway in north block of buildings . . . . . . *facing* 50

INTRODUCTION

Published descriptions of mediaeval castles generally deal exclusively with architectural and historical details, but such features as the sites, water supply and building-stones are comparatively neglected. Yet geological considerations enter, or should do so, in connection with all buildings of considerable size. There is the question of site, the choice of which varies with the purpose of the building ; and if a particular site is of paramount importance, its form (especially if irregular) may affect the final plan of the building. Closely connected with the site is the question of water supply which must often have been a serious problem in the days when distant sources could not be utilised by means of pipe lines. There is also the material of which the building is made, generally local stone, but sometimes brought from a distance.

These questions are pertinent in the case of all buildings of any size, such as churches, monasteries and mediaeval castles. In the choice of sites for churches, the water supply is not of first importance but in the case of monasteries the question enters largely, because such buildings housed considerable numbers of people. In the planning of mediaeval castles the three factors are of equal importance for the failure of one of them at a critical time might prove disastrous. In considering the water-supply it must be remembered that consumption of water before the 19th century was much less than now. Still an adequate supply of drinking water was always essential, and the most reliable supply would be from an underground source. The provision of such is a geological problem which is not always easy to solve. At Conway for instance the difficulties of an internal supply proved so great that a distant supply is said to have been connected by a pipe-line. In some cases the difficulty might be met by the more unreliable method of conserving rain water ; this, however, is an engineering rather than a geological question.

The present study is confined to the mediaeval castles of Wales north of the River Dee which have been personally examined for the purpose. Among the many friends who showed great interest during the progress of the work was the late W. L. Hobbs, a founder-member of the Dyserth and District Field Club, and a keen student of Archaeology and Geology. The Field Club has accorded to the writer the opportunity and privilege of offering this paper as a tribute to the memory of Mr. Hobbs.

The results of the work are arranged in the following manner. First a site of considerable importance in the history of North Wales, but of simple geological structure, is described in order to illustrate how the essential features have been utilised ; the site of Chester and of Beeston Castle furnish good examples. Then the broad geological features of North Wales are summarised to form a basis for discussion of the castle-sites. Finally, the sites of the castles are described in some detail, and for this purpose some classification is inevitable. The castles seem to arrange themselves in four groups : (1) the castle mounds of 11th and 12th century date, (2) the early English stone castles, (3) the Welsh stone castles, and (4) the so-called Edwardian castles of the 13th century. This grouping has the advantage of a more or less chronological arrangement, and each of the groups has certain geological features peculiar to itself.

CHAPTER I

GEOLOGICAL FEATURES OF THE CHESHIRE
BORDERLAND

Though not in Wales, the geological features of Chester may be considered as a fitting introduction to a discussion of Welsh castle-sites. The city stands on a site which attracted the attention of successive invaders (Roman, Norman and English) and so played a great part in the destinies of North Wales.

The old city of Chester stands on a ridge of red sandstone which passes through Alford, Eccleston, Chester and Whitby, in a direction which is approximately north and south. It is the most westerly of three ridges formed of the rock known as the Bunter Sandstone, the lowest division of the Triassic System. Another of these ridges passes through Tattenhall, Tarvin, Dunham and Hapsford ; the third, which is less distinct, through Saighton and Christleton. The dip in these hills is uniformly at low angles to the east, so that steep escarpments are formed on the western side. The ridges are apparently due to repetition of the Bunter sandstone by successive N—S faults which throw down the rocks to the west. The low ground between the ridges is deeply covered with the much younger Boulder Clay and other Glacial deposits.

The River Dee, after following the escarpment for some miles, cuts across it at Chester in a narrow steep-sided valley excavated entirely in the rock. There are frequent exposures in the banks above the Grosvenor Bridge, and the rock has been proved by tunnelling under the river at the Waterworks at Boughton.

Towards the low ground east of the city, a thin covering of Boulder Clay begins at the Eastgate and thickens eastwards. Near City Road a thin wedge of sand separates the clay from the rock and develops into the great sandy deposit which occurs at the surface around Boughton. The sand is overlapped where the Drift abuts against a rising surface of the Bunter sandstone.

In a sketch-plan of Chester in 1574, the River Dee is represented as turning more rapidly than at present after passing the Castle so as to flow past the Watergate and along the walls to the Water Tower, and as spreading out thence into a broad channel along what was formerly known as Finchett's Gutter. In consequence of silting up, the existing artificial course from Chester to Saltney and thence to Connah's Quay was made by the Dee Navigation Company in 1733–6. The change in the course from the Castle to the Water Tower appears to have resulted from the undermining of the bank on the outer (western) curve, and the simultaneous silting up of the inner side to the flood-level, a process which takes place in the lower course of most rivers. A large part of the Roodee has therefore come into existence during the last three centuries. The alluvium of the Roodee and Sealands consists of fine sand and loam with marine shells brought from the sea by the action of the tides. At the Gasworks, by the side of the L.M.S. railway, a section in 1880 showed five or six feet of sand and silt overlying Boulder Clay which was excavated to more than 25 feet (STRAHAN, 1882). More recently Professor R. Newstead has estimated that the Roodee site has silted up over 20 feet since the Roman occupation. The geological features of Chester therefore show a site formed of sandstone which has a gentle dip-slope to the east, and a steep escarpment of about 30 feet to the west, this and the southern side being, in addition, protected by a meander of the River Dee. (Map, Fig. 1).

The Bunter Sandstone is moderately hard and fine-grained, with well-rounded pebbles of liver-coloured and white quartz

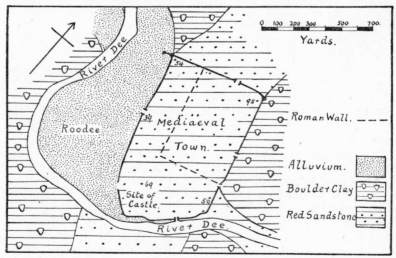

FIG. 1. Geological Sketch-map of Chester
(*based on Geol. Surv., Old Series, 80 S.W.*)

2

scattered through the rock, or forming shingly partings between beds of freestone. It has been quarried in many places for building purposes. Much stone used in the Cathedral and old Abbey buildings was obtained from quarries outside the North-gate and in places within the walls on the east side of Northgate Street. Most of these were abandoned long ago and built over, but the rock is still exposed in the railway and canal cuttings. The stone is not of first quality as building material, for it tends to become friable under the action of the weather. The period of endurance was thought by SHRUBSOLE (1887) to be not more than five centuries for large blocks fully exposed to atmospheric denudation. Hence, though the Romans doubtless used the stone, none of their work survives above the surface of the ground. There are records to show that the stone was quarried in mediaeval times, and E. W. COX (1895) regards the chapel known as Caesar's Tower as the sole remnant of the first mediaeval castle of Chester which was built about 1246. The present condition of St. John's Church Tower is an illustration of weathering action on the red sandstone. Still, the rock served the purpose of building material in successive centuries and its presence in the locality doubtless added to the attractions of the site for permanent occupation. Moreover, a short distance from Chester (at Manley, Peckforton, for instance) there is a harder and more durable stone belonging to the upper (Keuper) division of the Triassic System. This is said to have been used in the facing of the old city wall.

The Bunter Sandstone is a noted water-bearing rock throughout Cheshire and South Lancashire. There are some wells at Chester but the gathering ground is small because the rock has a narrow outcrop. Wells in Seller Street, King Street and Queen's Park are supplied from the sandstone, while in Bridge Street a small excavation in the rock, attributed to the Romans, contains water kept at a constant level, presumably from seepage through joints in the sandstone. The modern water supply is obtained from the River Dee nearly a mile north of the city but the river was probably not a source of potable water in the earlier centuries. Then it had a much greater volume and the tides reached further up the valley ; the water would be fresh only at low water, that is for only a few hours each day, and probably some other source of water was utilised. Earthern pipes of Roman type have been discovered in ex-cavations at various times, laid east and west towards Boughton. At this locality the sands and gravels underlying the Upper Boulder Clay are heavily charged with water which often overflows in springs. Such surface indications are readily seen and, according to SHRUBSOLE (1893), probably formed the main water supply for Roman Chester. There appears to be little evidence concerning the supply utilised by the Normans and English in mediaeval times. Plans of the mediaeval Castle given by E. W. Cox (1895) show positions of two wells, one in the first castle of Henry III, the other in the lower bailey added by Edward I. These wells presumably tapped the underground water in the red sandstone.

BEESTON CASTLE (1 inch Geological Map, Old Series 80 S.W.), 8 miles S.E. of Chester, provides an interesting site of smaller dimensions. The castle is built on an isolated crag of red sandstone which rises abruptly from the Drift-covered plain to a height of 500 ft. (Fig. 2). The lower part of the crag consists

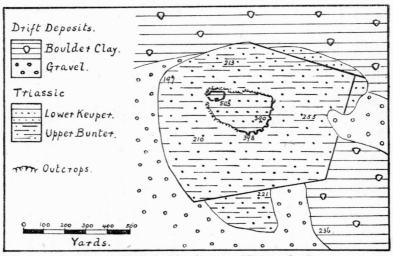

FIG. 2. Geological Sketch-map of Beeston Castle
(*based on Geol. Surv., Old Series, 80 S.W.*)

of sandstones assigned to the Upper Bunter Series, i.e., the division of the Trias next above the sandstones of Chester. The colour of the stone varies considerably, and abrupt variations are to be seen in several parts of the hill. The approach to the gateway of the outer fortifications on the east of the hill is cut in soft red sandstone ; the same beds on the north are chiefly yellow ; on the west the upper 6 ft. are yellow and the remainder red, while on the south the upper part is red and the lower composed of thick beds of white sands in which caves have been excavated. The red colour is due to a film of iron oxide which coats the sand grains and cements them into a coherent stone ;

the yellow and whitish tints are probably due to the action of percolating water.

At the old gateway on the east, and along the south and south-west of the crag, about 30 ft. below the south-western angle of the castle, the Upper Bunter is succeeded by Red sandstones which are classified as the Basement Beds of the Keuper Series. These red sandstones, harder than those of the Upper Bunter, dip consistently to the E.S.E., and about 50 ft. of them is seen on the eastern side of the hill. Hence the western side of the hill is a steep escarpment.

A higher division of the Keuper Series, namely the Keuper Marls, underlies the Drift in the brook to the north. Their presence here can only be explained by a fault, extending from west to east between the crag and the valley, which throws down the marls about 600 ft. to the north ; the fault, however, is concealed by the covering of Drift.

The Castle Crag may be regarded as an isolated portion of the Peckforton escarpment, and its isolation is due indirectly to the faults which enclose it on three sides. By these, the outcrop of Keuper Basement Beds is thrown against softer beds which are more easily removed by the agents of denudation. The basal fragment of Keuper sandstone is thus left isolated in a position which attracted the mediaeval castle-builders. Moreover, the Triassic sandstone forms suitable building material, and usually provides an adequate water-supply.

Chapter II

GENERAL GEOLOGICAL FEATURES OF NORTH WALES

Before discussing the castles in detail, it is advantageous to consider those broad geological features of North Wales which appertain to the present subject, especially the distribution of the solid rocks. On a general view the rocks are progressively older as one proceeds westwards, but the solid rocks are often concealed by superficial deposits (collectively termed Drift) especially on the lower ground, as for example the coastal plain between Flint and Abergele. The whole series is classified into Systems which are now briefly described in downward succession as far as they occur in North Wales; the map (Fig. 3) shows their distribution.

The newest deposits comprise the blown sand of the coastal margin and the alluvium of the river-valleys which are still in process of formation, and glacial deposits which were formed during the Great Ice Age. The latter are conveniently considered as of two types, namely, Boulder Clay and Gravels. The Boulder Clay forms an almost continuous cover on the low ground near the coast, but on the higher ground it is sporadic in distribution. The Boulder Clay is so named from the abundance of boulders, varying in size from mere pebbles to masses several tons in weight; some of these represent rocks which occur in the immediate vicinity, but many can only be ascribed to distant sources, particularly the country around Snowdon and northern areas such as the Lake District and southern Scotland. The northern erratics are restricted to the coastal margin. The boulders are embedded in a clay which varies in consistency and is often more or less sandy. The deposit represents the material embedded in ice-sheets or glaciers and left after the melting of the ice. The gravels are of similar origin, but contain much less of the fine-grained material. The Drift deposits (including the alluvium) are important in the present connection because they comprise the only non-consolidated rock-material in North Wales, and they obviously determine the distribution of the artificial mounds on which the early Norman castles were built. The boulders have only occasionally been used as building material; probably their rounded form was found unsuitable for the purpose. Criccieth Castle is remarkable for the number of boulders used in its construction, and the castle at Aber Lleiniog is built entirely of such material ; rounded boulders are present to a slight extent in the walls of the castles at Flint and Rhuddlan, but elsewhere they are rarely seen.

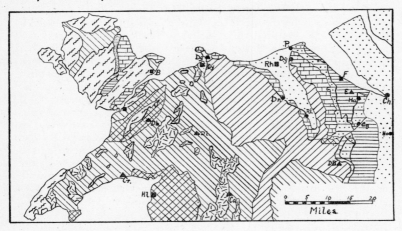

Key to Shading.

::::	Triassic
≡	Coal Measures
:::::	Millstone Grit
⊞	Carb. Limestone
▦	Old Red Sandstone
▨	Silurian.
▧	Ordovician.
▩	Cambrian
▨	Precambrian.

Carboniferous.

Localities.

Early English Stone Castles. ●

Caergwrle	Cg.	Chester	Ch.
Denbigh.	Dn.	Dyserth	Dy
Hawarden.	Ha.	Holt	Ho
Prestatyn.	P.	Ruthin.	Rt

Welsh Stone Castles. ▲

Carndochan	Ca.	Cticcieth.	Ct
Deganwy	Dg	Dolbadarn	Db.
Dolwyddelan	Dl	Ewloe	E
	Dinas Bran	DB	

Edwardian Castles. ■

Beaumaris	B.	Caernarvon	Cn.
Conway	Cy	Flint.	F.
Harlech	Hl	Rhuddlan.	Rh.

FIG. 3.   Geological Sketch-map of North Wales, showing location of Castles
(*based on Geol. Surv., Index Map, Sheet 9*)

The red sandstones of the Triassic System have already been mentioned as occurring in the vicinity of Chester. From that city they extend westward to the neighbourhood of Dodleston and Kinnerton, and southward by Holt to Overton. These sandstones are not often exposed at the surface in this district,

7

but Holt Castle stands on them. Similar Triassic rocks are again seen to form part of the solid floor of the Vale of Clwyd further west ; their occurrence here is due (at least in part) to repetition by faulting. Ruthin Castle stands on an outcrop of red sandstone which also furnished material for the building.

Between Chester and the Clwyd Hills the solid floor of the country is occupied by a varied succession of rocks assigned to the Carboniferous System. These rocks are readily divisible into three series : an upper series of shales and sandstones with workable coal-seams, known collectively as the Coal Measures, a middle series, the so-called Millstone Grit, embracing the Holywell Shales of Flintshire and the Cefn y fedw Sandstone of Denbighshire, and a lower series known as the Carboniferous Limestone. On the whole, these rocks all dip eastwards or north-eastwards, away from the high ground of the Clwyd Range. The two lower divisions are harder and more resistant to agents of denudation than the Coal Measures. In consequence of the dip and their softer character the last-named rocks come to occupy the lower ground to the east of the district though they are situated higher in the geological succession.

The Coal Measures are a series of sandstones, shales and coal-seams occupying the area of the Flintshire and Denbigh-shire coalfields. These rocks are largely concealed by a covering of Drift, but the sandstones occasionally reach the surface around Buckley, Connah's Quay, Flint and Mostyn in Flintshire, and at Cefn Mawr and Broughton in Denbighshire ; at other places the sandstones and shales are exposed by the erosion of valleys on their eastward slope, while the succession has been proved in the shafts of many collieries. The classification into Upper, Middle and Lower Coal Measures by grouping the coal-seams and other strata on the evidence of fossils obtained from them need not detain us. Naturally the coal-seams are described in geological literature in greatest detail because of their industrial importance, though their collective thickness is only about one-fifteenth of the total thickness of the whole series. But in connection with castles the sandstones are more important, for they form the foundation of several sites and they have also furnished building material. It therefore seems advisable to discuss briefly the scattered information regarding the sand-stones, for while the source of mediaeval building material cannot always be determined with precision, it can often be traced to a particular district by some peculiarity in the constitution of the rock, especially when the outcrops are limited as in the present instance. The horizons of the chief sandstones in the Carboniferous succession of Flintshire and Denbighshire are shown in the accompanying diagram. (Fig. 4).

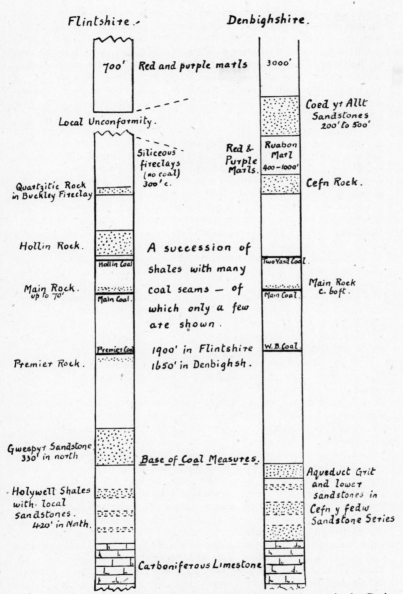

FIG. 4. Diagram Section to show position of the chief sandstones in the Coal Measures and Millstone Grit of North Wales.

9

The uppermost sandstones are seen in the Coed yr allt Group of Denbighshire. This rather varied group of strata includes massive beds of sandstone (sometimes more than 50 feet thick) which are well seen at Coed yr allt, opposite the junction of the rivers Ceiriog and Dee. The sandstones form escarpments which often rise through the Drift for some distance as in Wynnstay Park and east of Ruabon. The rock is a grey sandstone, sometimes coarse and felspathic, elsewhere shaly or compact.

Some distance lower in the succession, 400 to 1,000 feet according to locality, is the Cefn Rock which affords a well-known building stone. This buff-coloured fine-grained sandstone is typical of the Coal Measures sandstones generally. It is worked principally from its outcrop at Cefn Mawr (S.W. of Ruabon) and Broughton (N.W. of Wrexham) and some of the quarries are said to date from mediaeval times. Near the Dee it often reaches the surface and constitutes the dominant physical features. The Cefn Rock extends up to the northern margin of the Denbighshire coalfield. In Flintshire the same approximate horizon is occupied by the Buckley Fireclay group which also includes a sandstone. This, however, is very different from the Cefn Rock, for it is a hard, fine-grained, white, quartzitic sandstone which is associated with siliceous fireclays, but no coals are present. This development, only known in the Buckley area, provides a striking dissimilarity in the upper part of the Coal Measures between the Flintshire and Denbighshire coalfields.

Some distance below the Buckley Fireclay is the Hollin Rock which, like most sandstones in the Flintshire Coalfield, attains its greatest thickness (about 200 ft.) in the Buckley area. It persists in a thinner development throughout the Flintshire Coalfield wherever the upper part of the Coal Measures has escaped denudation. Perhaps the most notable occurrence of this rock in the present connection is in Wepre Wood, where a quarry on the east side of the dingle, 130 yards north of the junction of the streams below Ewloe Castle, shows 25 feet of red-stained sandstone (ascribed to the Hollin Rock) overlying purple shales ; a similar but distinctive sandstone is used for doorway jambs and window-casings in Ewloe Castle. The Hollin Rock thins out to the south and hardly extends to the Denbighshire Coalfield. Some 200 feet lower in the Flintshire succession a massive sandstone, the Main Rock, which reaches a thickness of 70 feet in places, is associated with the Main Coal in the Buckley district. In Denbighshire a similar sandstone also associated with the Main Coal occurs some 600 feet below the Cefn Rock. Another massive buff-coloured sandstone (up to 24 feet in thickness) is developed some little distance above the Yard Coal on the west side of the Buckley district ; this stone, known as the Yard Rock, contains quartz pebbles in its lower part. South of Bagillt and near Connah's Quay the Coal Measures below the Premier Coal include several strong beds of yellowish sandstone some of which contain pebbly seams. At Connah's Quay railway station 25 feet of this rock is seen lying on shales, and the massive Ewloe Castle rock, which is exposed for some distance up the dingle of Altami Brook is probably on the same horizon. The same sandstone is exposed in places on Flint Mountain, and also forms the foundation on which Flint Castle is built. The walls of Flint Castle and also of Basingwerk Abbey are made chiefly of yellowish sandstones (often with pebbly bands) typical of the Coal Measures generally.

At the base of the Coal Measures in North Flintshire is a massive sandstone which is best seen in the extensive quarries around the village of Gwespyr. Here the altitude of the mass, which ends a short distance northward in a steep cliff, indicates a thickness of at least 200 feet. Eastwards higher beds appear, and the Geological Survey estimates the total thickness of the Gwespyr Sandstone at about 330 feet. The main rock-beds, known commercially as the Talacre Stone, which are quarried for building purposes, are homogeneous fine-grained sandstones of a yellowish or buff colour and are unusually massive and compact for Coal Measures sandstones. They are often finely laminated, with wrinkled bedding, and sometimes contain large " bullions " or concretions of very hard sandstone which is slightly coarser in grain than the stone used for building purposes. The age of the beds is determined by the occurrence of goniatites of the *Gastrioceras listeri* group in the sandstone at Ffynnon groew while *Gastrioceras cancellatum* has been obtained from shales just below the sandstone. The Gwespyr Sandstone attains its greatest development between Gwespyr and Greenfield, occupying both the northern and southern limbs of a syncline which extends along a west to east line near the coast. It appears to have been worked by the Romans, judging by its occurrence in remains of a Roman building at Prestatyn (NEWSTEAD & NEAVERSON, 1937) and a block of the sandstone is to be seen in the fragmentary remains of Prestatyn Castle ; similar stone seems to have been transported as far west as Maenan Abbey in mediaeval times.

The middle division of the Carboniferous System in N. Wales, corresponding to the Millstone Grit of the English Midlands, comprises the Cefn y fedw Sandstone and the Holywell Shales. The Cefn y fedw Sandstone (not to be confused with the Cefn Rock of the Coal Measures) is best seen on Ruabon Mountain, formerly known as Cefn y fedw, from which the rock was named by G. H. MORTON (1870). The series, some 680 feet thick in the type area, is not entirely sandstone, for thick beds of shale separate four massive sandstones, the uppermost being known as the Aqueduct Grit. All the sandstones are fine-grained and light in colour ; those in the lower part of the series often enclose pebbles of quartz. The outcrop extends northward from Ruabon Mountain by Minera and Nerquis to the neighbourhood of Mold, and the series is repeated by faulting around Hope and Caergwrle.

The sandstone forms the hill on which Caergwrle Castle stands and furnished the material for the building of the castle. A faulted inlier occurs at Hawarden where the sandstones are exposed in many disused quarries near St. John's Lodge and in Bilberry Wood and give an almost continuous section for about half a mile. The maximum thickness near Hawarden is estimated at about 600 feet but some of the beds may be repeated by faulting. The pale-coloured sandstones of this locality were used for building the mediaeval castle near by. Around Holywell the equivalent rocks are shales with some thin interbedded sandstones and limestones, the whole being termed the Holywell Shales. Correlation with the Cefn y fedw Sandstone is possible, for the goniatites known as *Reticuloceras reticulatum* are found both in the upper part of the Holywell Shales and in shales just below the Aqueduct Grit at the Aqueduct, Tynant ravine and Nant y Frith (Minera). But lower in the series the Cefn y fedw sandstones have not yielded fossils similar to those of the Holywell Shales ; this may possibly be due to the different conditions under which the beds were deposited. At Prestatyn the lowest beds of the Holywell Shales are compacted into slabby limestones and rest on an uneven surface of Carboniferous Limestone. Pieces of these harder basal beds are present in the scanty remnant of Prestatyn Castle, which stands within a short distance of the outcrop.

The Carboniferous Limestone forms the eastern fringe of the Clwyd Range. From an altitude of 600 feet in the northern part of the outcrop which forms the Flintshire plateau near Caerwys and Holywell, it rises to nearly 1,300 ft. further south near Llanarmon where it forms a series of foothills with its beds dipping eastwards off the older rocks of the range. West of Mold its thickness has been estimated at over 2,500 feet. Near Minera the outcrop is displaced eastward by an extension of the Bala Fault, and forms the lofty escarpment known as the Eglwyseg Rocks north of Llangollen ; thence it becomes attenuated and swings south-eastwards to the River Dee. The

Limestone is seen further east as a faulted inlier which forms the Hope Hills. The same series of rocks also forms a fringe to the Denbighshire Moors, being repeated in effect by the Vale of Clwyd Fault-System, and extends in a series of blocks from Colwyn on the coast by Abergele, St. George, Denbigh and Ruthin to the vicinity of Llanelidan, where it is entirely cut off by a strong fault running from west to east.

In many places along these outcrops the compact varieties of the Carboniferous Limestones have been used as building stone. Denbigh Castle stands on a hill formed of the limestone which furnished the principal building material. Rhuddlan Castle is situated at some distance from the outcrop, but Carboniferous Limestone forms a considerable part of its walls. The castles of Prestatyn and Dyserth were largely built of the same material judging by the poor remnants now existing. The limestone and associated beds of sandstone in Anglesey and on the mainland near the Menai Strait were used largely for the castle-walls at Caernarvon and Beaumaris. The castle at Aber Lleiniog in Anglesey is also built of the same material, but in this case the blocks of limestone were not quarried ; they were obtained from the glacial drift which in this neighbourhood encloses large erratic blocks of Carboniferous Limestone derived from outcrops to the north.

Like most of the solid rocks in North Wales the Carboniferous Limestone is considerably broken by faults due to local adjustment after movements of the earth's crust. Many of the fissures have subsequently been filled with various minerals deposited in the form of veins or lodes, calcite (commonly known as ' spar ') and galena being the most widely distributed. Galena has long been worked as a source of lead, and various historical records (e.g., The Black Prince's Register Parts I & III) refer to the smelting of lead from mines around Halkyn and Faenol (Bodelwyddan) for use in roofing the castles of Edward I.

In a large tract of country extending from eastern Shropshire through Herefordshire and Monmouthshire into South Wales the Carboniferous System is followed in downward succession by the non-marine Old Red Sandstone, which attains a thickness of some 4,500 feet. Apart from a small outcrop in Anglesey, this formation is absent in North Wales where the Carboniferous Limestone rests uncomformably on rocks of the Silurian System. But though the rocks are absent, the period of time which they represent is of considerable importance with regard to the texture and tectonic structure of the older rocks. For it was a period of earth-movement during which the older strata were faulted and folded, while the intense pressure acting in a tangential direction imposed a strong cleavage on the finer-grained rocks which thus acquired a slaty texture. The cleavage affects the Silurian and older rocks, but not the Carboniferous strata ; hence it was imposed in the intervening period.

Rocks of the Silurian System underlie the vast area of the Clwyd Range and the Denbighshire Moors, extending westwards as far as the valley of the Conway, and even beyond that limit around the estuary of that river. The dominant rocks are fine-grained shales, often compacted into mudstones and always affected in greater or less degree by the cleavage described above. At intervals in the succession (probably approaching 5,000 feet in thickness in the southern part of the area) strong grits are interbedded with shales, and usually the grits have proved competent to resist the cleavage. Only two mediaeval castles are situated on these rocks, namely Conway Castle and Castell Dinas Bran near Llangollen, both on the margin of the area. The latter stands on an isolated hill formed of the mudstones which provided the indifferent material of which it is built. Conway Castle stands on a narrow outcrop of Silurian grit which also forms the principal building material for its walls. The elevated plateau of the Denbighshire Moors, with deep valleys eroded in the Drift deposits, sometimes through to the Silurian shales below, and considerable hills formed by the more resistant grits, was evidently not favoured for military operations by the mediaeval invaders, and this may account for the absence of stone castles throughout the area.

West of the Conway Valley is a large area occupied by rocks of the Ordovician System. From Deganwy and Conway in the north it extends through to the Snowdon country thence south-westward to the peninsula of Lleyn and southward through the Arenig and Aran Mountains to Cader Idris and beyond. Hence the Ordovician strata nearly surround the great Harlech Dome which is formed of older rocks. From the Arenig mountains an eastward extension forms the core of an anticline as far as Derwen in Denbighshire, while an isolated outcrop forms the hill of Cyrn y Brain at the south-east of the Clwyd range. The system is specially notable for the great thicknesses of volcanic rocks which are intercalated with the sedimentary strata. The latter are mainly dark-coloured shales usually compacted and hardened by cleavage ; shaly limestones occur at some horizons. Most of the volcanic rocks fall into the class known as tuffs which have been formed by volcanic dust falling into water and settling down as sediment ; thus, although they are composed of volcanic material, tuffs resemble sediment-ary rocks in their regular arrangement in strata. Moreover, tuffs often contain fossil shells which were entombed in the falling dust ; the marine shells often found in tuffs at the summit

14

of Snowdon afford a well-known example. The tuffs are harder than shales and are more resistant to processes of weathering ; consequently they stand out in bold relief, as the mountains of Snowdon, Arenig, Aran and Cader Idris, and so determine the diversified character of the scenery for which this region is justly famous. This is pre-eminently the domain of the Welsh castles including Deganwy, Dolwyddelan, Carndochan and Criccieth. These are all founded on hills formed of volcanic rocks and their walls are built of the same intractable stones. The English castle of Caernarvon is situated on an outcrop of Ordovician shales, but the rocks of this system occupy only a minor place among its building materials.

The most conspicuous occurrence of rocks assigned to the Cambrian System lies west of the Arenigs and Arans, between these mountains and the coast. This is the well-known Harlech Dome which exposes the grandest mass of the older Cambrian rocks in the country. These comprise three great stages of shales and slates separated by two stages of massive grits, the succession attaining a total thickness of more than 5,000 feet. Harlech Castle is situated on a prominent spur of Harlech Grit on the north-western margin of the dome, and its walls are built of the same grit obtained from quarries near by. The spur, like many other physical features of the dome, seems to be determined by joint-planes and minor faults. Around the margin of the dome, from Criccieth and Portmadoc by Festiniog to Cader Idris, younger Cambrian rocks (mainly cleaved shales) crop out in successive rings which can be traced with fair regularity, though they are often broken and distorted. Another important area of Cambrian strata surrounds a ridge of Precambrian rocks which extends from Bethesda to Llanllyfni. The Cambrian rocks here are highly cleaved, fine-grained slates which are well-known from their exploitation at Llanberis and Bethesda for roofing material. Dolbadarn Castle near Llanberis, which commands a pass into the Snowdon country, is situated in this slate-belt, and is built of thin-bedded grit obtained from the same series of rocks.

Beneath the Cambrian System there are still older rocks which are extremely variable in texture and composition. Members of the group are very difficult to place in chronological order and the series is generally referred to simply as Precambrian. Two ridges of these rocks occur on the mainland of Wales. One extends from the neighbourhood of Bethesda south-westward to Llanllyfni and consists of a uniform series of volcanic rocks known as felsite. The second ridge lies near the coast between Bangor and Caernarvon ; at the northern end is a series of tuffs and conglomerates which are associated near Caernarvon with the so-called granite of Twt Hill. Precambrian rocks form the preglacial surface of more than half of Anglesey and may conveniently be grouped into three types. The first, which is probably the youngest, is a volcanic series which compares in general terms with those of the mainland. Another group is distinguished by its prevalent green colour ; it is a monotonous group of foliated schists which are probably metamorphosed sedimentary rocks. The third type is a coarsely crystalline gneiss which also has a foliation induced by intense pressure during metamorphism. These rocks are of minor importance in the present study, for no castles stand upon their outcrops. Moreover, the irregular surfaces and splintery edges of the foliated rocks render them generally unsuitable for building purposes ; the lower courses of the castle walls at Beaumaris, however, contain large blocks of green schist which were probably obtained from the nearby outcrop.

The locations of the stone-built castles on the respective geological systems are plotted on the accompanying sketch-map (Fig. 3). The distribution of the rocks is shown in greater detail on the useful ¼-inch Index Map (Sheet 9) of the Geological Survey, and on the standard one-inch maps of the same authority. For purposes of reference the numbers of the appropriate geological maps are quoted in the text together with those of the six-inch Ordnance maps. In a few instances where the maps of the Geological Survey are in need of revision, reference is made to the work of more recent authors. Thus, Figs. 1-3, 5, 6, 9 and 13 are based on the published maps of the Geological Survey; Fig. 14 is drawn from a map by WILLIAMS & BULMAN (1931), Fig. 19 from ELLES (1909), and Fig. 20 from GREENLY (1943). Photographs by Judges Ltd. are reproduced in Figs. 8, 12, and 18, others by Valentine in Figs. 16 and 17. Permission to use this material is hereby gratefully acknowledged.

CHAPTER III

CASTLE-MOUNDS WITHOUT BUILDINGS

In their attempt to subjugate Wales during the 11th and
12th centuries the Normans erected castles at frequent points
along their lines of penetration. The castles were of the motte
and bailey type, founded on a flat-topped mound generally
artificially made of earth, but sometimes fashioned out of a
natural hillock, and, in either case, surrounded by a ditch.
On the summit of the mound was built a tower of timber, and
at its base was a courtyard or bailey also ditched and surrounded
by a timber stockade. The wooden structures have long since
disappeared, as also in many cases have the ditches and en-
closures ; the mound is usually the only existing relic.

The construction of these strongholds requires the presence
of a suitable substratum which could be rapidly fashioned into
conical mounds. Hence the distribution of Norman castles is
limited in general by the presence of Drift deposits, the only
non-consolidated rocks in North Wales. As mentioned earlier,
the Drift deposits are thickest on the low lands of the coastal
plain and in the river valleys. These are the routes along which
the Normans advanced and the castle-mounds are usually
restricted to these situations. Along the coastal route from
Chester into Wales there are mounds at Dodleston (Cheshire),
Hawarden, Holywell and Rhuddlan, a series of strongholds
capable of controlling the large part of Flintshire which came
under the dominance of the Norman earl of Chester within a
few years after 1066. The first three are made of Boulder Clay,
while Twt Hill at Rhuddlan is a conical mound built of the
silty alluvium deposited by the River Clwyd. Before 1088,
Robert of Rhuddlan built a castle at Deganwy on an isolated
hill formed of volcanic rock. This is exceptional, for the
Normans seem to have avoided building on solid rock whenever
possible ; presumably in this case the hillock happened to have
the desired shape and situation. Further west, the mound of
Aber was probably fashioned during this period, (though it was
afterwards used as a retreat by Llewelyn the Great), and a
Norman mound is said to have existed until recent years in the
enclosure of Caernarvon Castle (PEERS, 1932). Two mounds
at Aber Lleiniog, north of Beaumaris in Anglesey, appear to
represent the most north-westerly point occupied by the
Normans. One of them, on the coast at the mouth of the

17

stream, commands a landing place. The other, half a mile inland, has a square fort of stone on its summit, usually held to have been erected in 1089. While HOLME (in W. B. LOWE, 1927) says that the "origin, date and early history are fully authenticated," ARMITAGE (1912) suggests that the stonework was "probably built to carry guns at the time of the Civil War." The walls are built almost entirely of Carboniferous Limestone, large blocks of which (some 3 feet across) often form the entire thickness of the wall. They are mostly rectangular boulders with rounded edges, and a few smaller and more rounded boulders of dolerite are to be seen. The rounded edges account for the wide joints in the wall noted by HOLME. The aggregate of the mortar is similar to the gravel on the nearby shore. The limestone was evidently brought from the shore where similar large blocks are abundant, having been washed out of the Boulder Clay cliff by the sea. Hence no quarrying was required and (it may be suggested) the transport of the stone would involve less time and labour than the felling and carrying of timber. This would account for the building of a stone castle at a date when most castles were made of timber. But if the Norman date of mound and stonework be assumed there remains the difficulty that settlement of the foundations would be expected on the (as yet) unstable mound.

One of the most famous Norman mounds further inland is the Bailey Hill at Mold, 400 feet above sea level, which stands on a south-eastward ridge of Glacial Gravel, and overlooks the valley of the River Alyn to the north, and fairly flat country occupied by Boulder Clay to the south-west and west. STRAHAN (1890) describes this mound as "the most conspicuous Drift feature of the neighbourhood" and "a fine example of a sand and gravel esker, though its original form has been modified artificially." Within three miles are the smaller mounds of Tyddyn and Leeswood. Eight miles south-east of Mold, connecting also with Pulford and Chester, is the Rofft Mount near Gresford, which ARMITAGE identifies with Hodesley of the Pipe Rolls. Five miles south of the Rofft is the mound of Erddig, south of Wrexham, which is said to be the only un-doubted example of a Norman-built mound within the confines of modern Denbighshire. All of these are built of Glacial sands and Gravels which form elevations overlooking river-valleys and the valleys provided the easiest routes into the uplands of Wales.

On the foothills of the Clwyd Range there are two mounds, Tomen y Vaerdre and Tomen y Rhodwydd, which were probably built to command routes through the range into the Vale of Clwyd. Even at the present day the lower part of the

Vale (around Rhuddlan and Rhyl) is marshy, and was probably dangerously so in Norman times. The Vale was therefore entered at the south, by the defile near Llandegla (now called Nant y Garth). To command this pass Owain Gwynedd built the Tomen y Rhodwydd in 1149 after capturing Mold three years earlier. This great mound, 66 feet in diameter and 24 feet high, stands in an enclosure about an acre in extent. The Drift deposits here are of limited superficial extent, for outcrops of solid rock (Carboniferous Limestone) occur within 300 yards on east, north and south-west of the mound, and within ½ mile to the west is the high ground formed of Silurian mudstones.

At Llanarmon yn Ial, three miles further north, the Tomen y Vaerdre commands the passage of the river Alun. The mound (80 feet in diameter and 30 feet high) is built of alluvium deposited by the river, and the ditch on the eastern side is cut in the solid Carboniferous Limestone. The building of this Mound is attributed to the Norman earl of Chester ; the castle was burned by Iowerth Goch of Powys in 1157 and restored by John in 1212 (LLOYD 1912).

Later, the English essayed a more direct route along the ancient road between Moel Fammau and Moel Fenlli. The Welsh mound of Llys Gwenllian, one mile south of Denbigh, is said to have been built by Llewelyn ap Iowerth to counteract this movement. The site of Llys Gwenllian is a little hill at the confluence of a small stream with the Afon Ystrad. The junction of the two streams forms the main strength of the position, though the hill is 100 feet higher than the confluence. In this neighbourhood thick deposits of glacial material conceal the solid rock.

Another route into the heart of Wales was afforded by the old Roman road from Oswestry across the Berwyn to the valley of the Dee, and on, by the valleys of the Afon Tryweryn and Afon Prysor, to Mur Castell near Trawsfynydd. Historical records attest the presence of William Rufus at Mur Castell in 1095, and this was also the meeting place for the armies of Henry I in 1114 (LLOYD 1912). There is little doubt that on one of these occasions the great mound known as Tomen y Mur, still 30 feet in height, and 300 feet in diameter, was built by the Normans within the enclosure of a Roman camp. The site is 900 feet above sea level, and 200 feet above the floor of the broad valley which it overlooks to the west (Fig. 7).

On the same route, about three miles to the south-east, is the mound known as Castell Prysor, said to have been built by a Welsh chieftain in reply to Tomen y Mur. This is built to a height of about 25 feet on the side of the stony valley of

19

Cwm Prysor, east of Trawsfynydd. Abundant material for the mound is furnished by the Boulder clay of the locality, and the sides of the mound are faced with boulders.

The route also includes the valley of the Dee from Corwen to Bala, a sector which is remarkable for the number of mounds still surviving. Some of these were doubtless built by the Normans, for the Vale of Edeyrnion was an important strategic point on the route. Just west of Corwen, near the junction of the River Alwen with the Dee, there is an open plain, some two square miles in extent, surrounded by an amphitheatre of hills. The southern part of the area (around Gwerclas and Llangar) is occupied by the present flood-plain of the two rivers, which is limited on the north by a steep bluff (map, Fig. 5). The northern part is a gently undulating plain of gravel which is (on the average) about 550 feet above sea-level, or 100 feet above the alluvial plain of the Dee at Corwen. The gravel plain is about 1½ miles wide near the rivers, but it narrows northwards where it extends for about the same distance towards Gwyddelwern. Similar gravels occur on both flanks of the flood-plain in the Dee valley east of Corwen. BERNARD SMITH (1919) considers the deposit to have been formed as marginal and terminal gravels during the retreating stages of the Dee Valley Glacier which filled the Corwen amphitheatre and thrust out

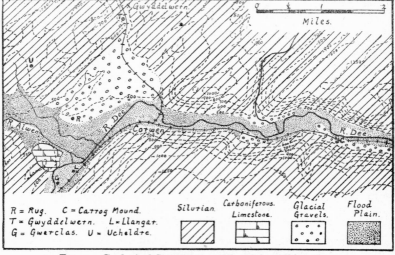

FIG. 5. Geological Sketch-map of the Vale of Edeyrnion
with location of Castle mounds
(*based partly on Geol. Surv., New Series, 121*)

20

branches northward and eastward. A prolonged halt, or slow melting during retreat, favoured the accumulation of a broad gravel-fan, the drainage escaping eastward down the valley of the Dee. The mounds of Gwerclas and Llangar are situated on the recent flood-plain, while Carrog Mount near Glyndyfrdwy and the mounds of Rug and Gwyddelwern are on the glacial flood-gravels. These were probably built by the Normans, for Gryffydd ap Cynan was captured at Rug in 1081 (LLOYD 1912) ; but after the withdrawal of the invaders on account of the difficult country and the defensive policy of Owen Gwynedd, they were occupied by Welsh chieftains. The mounds of Bala and Castell Gronw, built on the broad alluvial flat at the eastern end of Bala Lake are also most likely of Norman origin. It is reasonable to suppose, however, that others were made by the Welsh chieftains in opposition to, or in imitation of the Norman strongholds. A mound behind the house of Crogen, 2 miles east of Llanderfel, marks the castle of Elise ap Madog to which he retired after his defeat by Llewelyn the Great in 1202. It stands on a promontory of Ordovician mudstone which forms the core of a meander of the River Dee ; the lower part of the structure is a boss of the solid rock which dips to the north-west at about 20° ; the upper part is of earth and is about 36 feet in diameter. Within a comparatively short distance there are other mounds, at Hendwr, Llanfor, Ucheldre and Llangwm, while some eight miles north-west of the last-named there is the mound of Foel Las on the margin of the Denbighshire moors.

The importance of water supply for the occupants of these strongholds is obvious, and some writers (e.g., ARMITAGE, 1912), have stated that usually a well was constructed within the motte. Wells are said to have been found in a number of mottes in England which have been excavated, but no discovery of this kind in North Wales is known to the writer. It is felt that the provision and maintenance of such a supply in an artificial mound would be a matter of some difficulty ; more likely, reliance was placed on some external source near by, such as a natural spring or a stream.

CHAPTER IV

THE EARLY ENGLISH STONE CASTLES

During the 12th century stone gradually replaced wood for castle-building, though some castles of the older type continued to be erected and many survived all through the century. The early English stone castles in North Wales are confined to the eastern part of the country, for the region west of the Vale of Clwyd was never permanently occupied by the invaders. In most cases they stand on conspicuous hills, chosen for their natural suitability for defence and for their utility as observation posts. The development of these sites by the age-long action of geological processes furnishes an interesting study.

The design of stone castles developed along several different lines. The first development, during the 12th century, was the obvious one of building a large stone keep to replace the older wooden tower on the mound. On a site of limited extent the keep would be isolated within the enclosure (as was perhaps the case at Prestatyn Castle), or built at some point along the circuit of the wall. Sometimes when the site was too large to cover with a solid keep, the palisade of the mound was replaced by a wall of stone without towers, forming what is known as a shell-keep. During the same period the outer palisade of the bailey was also being replaced by simple curtain walls of stone which took the line of the original earthwork and ditch. Later, during the 13th century, the curtain walls were provided with mural towers, which afterwards developed into bastions ; these furnished a means of attacking a besieging force from within. The castles of Dyserth and Holt were of this type, but nothing is visible now. Concurrently a strong gatehouse became a prominent feature in castle-design, and subsidiary buildings were often erected within the walls. The massive gate-house at Denbigh Castle is an outstanding example. By the 14th century, a more symmetrical design had developed, with two or more lines of defence each protecting that immediately within it. This so-called " concentric " type, most prominently displayed in the group of castles which Edward I built in North Wales, is discussed in a separate chapter.

PRESTATYN CASTLE
6 in. Ordnance map. Flintshire 2 S.W.
1 in. Geological map. Old Series 79 N.W.
Flintshire Inventory 1912. LOWE, W. B. 1927. p. 187.

Little besides the mound of this castle now exists ; according to historical records it was built in 1164, and destroyed by the

Welsh three years later. The site is about ½ mile E.N.E. of Prestatyn Railway Station at a height of about 20 feet above sea level. It stands on Drift deposits which form the superficial cover on the coastal plain ; less than half a mile to the south, rocks of the Carboniferous system form hills which rise to a height of 400 feet. The mound is only about 3 feet above the surrounding country and therefore offers no obstacle to an attacking force ; as the adjacent ground is waterlogged in wet seasons, the mound was probably made rather for the purpose of keeping the building reasonably dry than for defence. Of the building only a small portion of the foundation is visible at the N.W. corner. This is made of fairly large rectangular blocks of grey limestone and yellowish sandstone, together with small pieces of thin-bedded black limestone, all of local origin. The grey limestone is well developed on the hillside south and south-west of Prestatyn where it has been quarried to a considerable extent. The sandstone may well have come from Gwespyr or Talacre, about 2 miles west of Prestatyn where similar stone is quarried for building and other purposes at the present time. The black limestone, which occurs at the base of the Holywell Shales, is exposed on the hillside above the castle site about ¼ mile distant. Water was doubtless obtained from wells dug in the Drift. Alternatively an overflow stream from the Nant Mill brook, such as that which now flows immediately west of the site may have been utilised ; the yield appears to be constant, and it probably arises from a spring in the hillside above.

DYSERTH CASTLE

6 in. Ordnance map. Flintshire 4 N.E.
Geological map. NEAVERSON. 1930.
Flintshire Inventory 1912. EDWARDS. 1912.

This castle was built by order of Henry III in 1241 and was destroyed by the Welsh in 1263. A considerable part of the ruin existed until 1916 but has since been obliterated by quarrying operations. Fortunately the castle was described in some detail by EDWARDS in 1912.

The castle stood on a spur of Carboniferous Limestone (known as Graig bach) about 400 ft. above sea level, which overlooks the northern end of the Vale of Clwyd and commands the inland route from Rhuddlan on the coast to Holywell and Chester. The site is precipitous on the south and west, but on the north is overlooked by the high ground of Graig fawr which rises to a height of 500 ft. EDWARDS' description shows that the strongest defences were built in this direction.

The source of water supply is indicated by the well-tower in the south-east portion of the castle (EDWARDS' plan 1912). The Carboniferous Limestone is not reliable for storage of water, but there is the possibility that fine material along a fault-plane sealed a pocket in which water collected. A north-south fault is conspicuous in the quarry below the site.

Only a few fragments of the rubble masonry are now to be seen. These consist of roughly hewn blocks of Carboniferous Limestone with a liberal infilling of mortar. The stone is similar to that now worked in the quarry below the south of the castle site. It is much shattered by faulting and is veined with calcite ; consequently it is not so good for building purposes as the compact stone now quarried at Dyserth only half a mile away to the south. Probably the inferior stone on the site was used in order to avoid the labour and cost of transport. It is not possible to verify EDWARDS' statement that " windows, door-casings and quoins are of a fine white freestone, probably brought from Storeton near Birkenhead. The masons' marks are identical with many in Bebington though of a later period, and might indicate the employment of Wirral masons." It may be mentioned however that the late W. L. Hobbs once told the writer that he had seen these stones.

HOLT CASTLE
 6 in. Ordnance map. Cheshire 53 S.E.
 1 in. Geological map. Old Series 73 N.W.
 Description—Denbighshire Inventory 1914.

The present village of Holt stands on the southern end of a ridge of Bunter Sandstone which extends through Farndon and some distance northwards. East of Holt the outcrop ends abruptly at the left bank of the River Dee, where a cliff, running slightly east of north, marks a line of fault that swings to the north and probably continues some distance beyond Farndon.

The site of the 13th century castle is formed by a boss of the red sandstone which has been isolated by the quarrying back of the cliff at this point. Excavation of the cliff has thus formed a defensive ditch besides furnishing building material for the castle. The latter stands at about 50 ft. above sea level and commands the passage of the Dee, but the ground immediately west of the castle is 10 to 15 ft. higher, for the rock dips eastward at a slight angle. The cramped nature of the site probably determined the form of the castle, which is that of a pentagonal curtain wall with sides about 50 ft. long, and round towers at the angles. A well was made in the small inner bailey and, as usual in the Triassic sandstones, probably yielded an adequate supply of water. The red sandstone of the site furnished the only building material now visible.

RUTHIN CASTLE

6 in. Ordnance map. Denbighshire 19 N.E.
1 in. Geological map. New Series, Sheet 108.
Denbighshire Inventory 1914.

The fragmentary remains of this 13th century castle stand on a ridge of red sandstone, assigned to the Bunter division of the Triassic System, a rock very similar in general constitution to that of Holt. The ridge rises about 100 ft. above the Clwyd Valley and overlooks lower ground to the west. The alignment of the ridge from N.E. to S.W. determines the main axis of the castle which was built in the form of an irregular pentagon. The building stone, a rather soft red sandstone, was probably quarried on the site (there is still a ditch on the north side) and its colour caused the building to be known as Castell Goch (red castle).

The Triassic sandstones of the Vale of Clwyd are yielding good supplies of excellent water at several places at the present time. A boring in Ruthin, a short distance from the castle was sunk nearly 400 ft. in the Trias and the supply has been used in the manufacture of aerated water. A shallow well on the castle site would therefore be expected to yield a supply adequate for the small garrison.

HAWARDEN CASTLE

6 in. Ordnance map. Flintshire 14 N.E.
Geological map. New Series, Sheet 108.
Flintshire Inventory 1912. CLARK, T. H. 1884.

This castle is situated on the first high ground west of Chester on the coast route into North Wales. The site is just above the 200 ft. contour line, overlooking flat country to the north and east, but there is higher ground (rising to 400 ft.) within two-thirds of a mile to the south-west. The ruins stand at the south-western end of a ridge of Glacial sands which descends by a steep slope (except on the north-east) to a small ravine 100 ft. below. The natural slope is modified by irregular banks and ditches. The stone keep occupies a steep-sided, conical mound, 30 ft. high, with a summit-diameter of 70 ft., which was probably made to support the Norman castle built by Hugh of Chester. The existing ruins are said to date from the end of the 13th century.

The well has not been discovered, but its location is suspected in the N.E. Ward. The Glacial Gravels and Sands are likely to have yielded an adequate supply, especially where those deposits rest on impervious Holywell Shales which are exposed in the banks of the stream a short distance south of the castle. The stream-section also reveals that the outcrop of the Holywell Shales is interrupted by a faulted block of Cefn y fedw Sandstone. If the trend of the fault-lines carry this sandstone beneath the castle there is the possibilty that a deep well may have yielded water in greater quantity (map, Fig. 6).

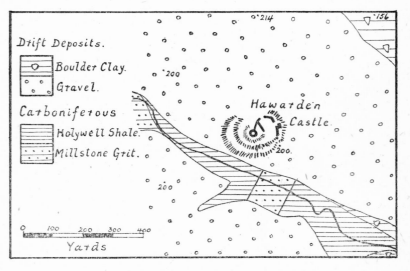

FIG. 6.   Geological Sketch-map of Hawarden Castle

(*based on Geol. Surv., New Series, 108*)

The circular keep, 60 ft. in diameter at the base, is of unusual solidity, the lower part of the wall being 15 ft. thick.   The bulk of the building material is a pale-coloured sandstone which varies somewhat in colour and texture.   Some of the blocks are almost quartzitic, while others contain rounded pebbles of quartz which give the stone a conglomeratic character.   A little above the ground there is a double bonding course of large ashlar blocks of yellow sandstone, and the original door and window-frames are made of the same material : it is softer and therefore easier to work than the quartzitic sandstone.·   All the building material can be matched in quarries to the south-west of the site, where the Cefn y fedw Sandstone shows similar variations in colour and texture.

26

FIG. 7. Tomen y Mur, view from the south   (*Photo E.N.*)

FIG. 8. Denbigh Castle viewed from west of the town.   (*Photo E.N.*)

6 in. Ordnance map. Flintshire 17 S.E.
1 in. Geological map. New Series, Sheet 108.
Flintshire Inventory 1912.

One of the most remarkable structural features of North
Wales is a great line of dislocation known as the Bala Fault
System, the effects of which can be traced from the neighbourhood
of Dolgelley, by Bala and Corwen to Caergwrle. Near the last
named village the effect is to truncate an anticline which brings
Cefn y fedw Sandstone and Carboniferous Limestone to the surface in the middle of the Flintshire Coalfield. As the soft shales
of the Coal Measures are denuded more rapidly than the more
resistant sandstones and limestones the latter (though older)
now stand at a higher topographical level than the former.
More particularly, the Hope Hills (formed of Carboniferous
Limestone and sandstone) rise to an altitude of 1,000 ft., that is,
some 500 or 600 feet above the average of the surrounding Coal
Measures. A deep valley separates the Hope Hills from the site
of Caergwrle Castle which is a bold hill of sandstone forming a
steep-sided spur at the eastern limit of the anticline. The site
is an excellent viewpoint, Buckley and Hawarden to the north,
the Peckforton Hills and Beeston Castle to the east being plainly

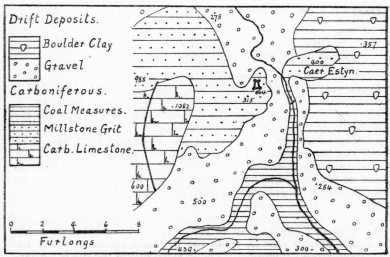

FIG. 9. Geological Sketch-map of the country around Caergwrle Castle
(based on Geol. Surv., New Series, 108)

C

visible, while the Wrekin can be distinguished when conditions are favourable. The hill rises about 100 feet above the river Alyn which separates it from the similar hill of Caer Estyn on the eastern bank of the stream. Both hills consist of the pale-coloured pebbly rock known as the Cefn y fedw Sandstone which is equivalent of the Millstone Grit of England ; the dip is towards the north-east. The rock furnishes building stone for the castle and also aggregate for mortar, and the material is said to have been obtained from old quarries still to be seen on the south of the hill.

The Cefn y fedw Sandstone is capricious with regard to water supply probably because of the varied character of the rock. Where the sand-grains are bound together by calcareous material, the latter is often dissolved by meteoric water, the rock is locally disintegrated and cavities are formed ; hence the water percolates to lower levels and is lost to human utility. This condition is seen along the dry sandstone hills south of Mold. But even there, occasional springs maintain a constant yield where an impervious bed intercepts the percolating water. Such a spring is said to supply the well at Caergwrle Castle, the spring being situated along the line of the small fault through the hill.

DENBIGH CASTLE

6 in. Ordnance map. Denbighshire 13 N.E.
1 in. Geological map. Old Series, Sheet 79 S.W.
Denbighshire Inventory 1914. HEMP. 1926.

The castle and town-wall are built on a hill, rising to 468 ft. above sea level, overlooking the Vale of Clwyd. The hill is composed of Carboniferous Limestone which dips about 12° to 15° to the N.N.E. ; hence the northern slope is gentle while the southern end is a steep scarp determined by the nearly vertical jointing of the rock. Moreover the limestone is underlain by soft red sandstones which here form the basement beds of the Carboniferous System ; these offer less resistance to weathering and so occupy lower ground (about 350 ft. above O.D.) to the south which is largely covered by Boulder Clay (Figs. 8/11). The precipice on the east of the site lies along a pronounced line of dislocation, one of several which determine the present form of the Vale of Clwyd. East of this line the red sandstones of the Triassic System now lie some 200 ft. below the local top of the Carboniferous Limestone. The western side of the site is perhaps determined by a small local dislocation connected with the fault which trends north-eastward towards the Vale of Clwyd.

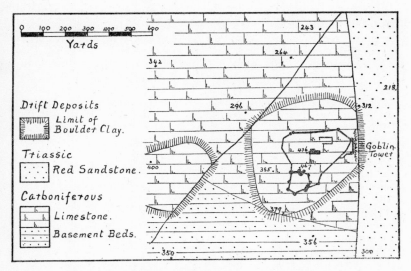

FIG. 10.   Geological Sketch-map of Denbigh showing Castle and walled town
(*adapted from Neaverson, 1945*)

HEMP notes a conspicuous difference in design of the N.E.
and S.E. sides as compared with N.W. and S.W. sides of the castle.
The latter have half-round towers connected by relatively thin
curtain-walls continuing the line of the Town Wall at the
highest and least accessible part of the site.   The N.E. and S.E.
sides of the castle have angular and elaborately planned towers,
and the curtain-walls are of much greater height and thickness ;
moreover the extremely elaborate gatehouse is in this sector.
While, as HEMP suggests, this contrast in design may point to a
different date of construction, it is significant that these structural
differences may be correlated with the topographical features
of the site ; the more elaborate defences would naturally be
required on the gentle slopes of the N.E. and S.E. sides.

The Carboniferous Limestone is not a water-bearing formation except sometimes in solution channels, which, however, are
not known to occur in Denbigh.   Moreover, the many joints in
the rock probably provide channels of escape.   Hence the well
in the Castle must always have been unreliable unless it was
sufficiently deep to reach the red basement beds or the Silurian
rocks below, and the known depth of the well (50 ft.) is far less
than would be required.   The mediaeval records of unreliability
(see HEMP 1926) are therefore not surprising.   The Triassic

29

sandstones of the Vale of Clwyd are noted for their water-bearing qualities, and they are the source of Denbigh's present supply. A second well was made on the eastern part of the town-wall and sheltered by the Goblin Tower which stands on the red sandstones. This tower was the main objective of besieging forces in 1648, according to contemporary records quoted by HEMP (1926) ; it is built against the fault-plane of the limestone and a short distance to the east red Triassic sandstone is known to occur just below the surface of the ground. It should be stated, however, that the details of underground geology at this point are imperfectly known.

The main building material is the Carboniferous Limestone which is an admirable stone of good wearing properties ; it was doubtless quarried not far away, and HEMP suggests the rock-cut ditch as one source of supply during the reconditioning after 1294. Red sandstone was freely used in the construction of the Red Tower at the north-west angle of the castle, and quoins of similar stone are seen elsewhere. This material was probably obtained from the Triassic rocks east of the site, though the precise location cannot now be indicated. Some of the ashlar blocks in the Red Tower belong to the Carboniferous Purple Sandstone of which the only adequate outcrop is near Pont yr allt goch, three miles north of Denbigh (NEAVERSON 1945). The same rock is represented by smaller, often irregular, pieces associated with the Triassic red sandstone in other parts of the castle. A fine-grained, greenish-yellow sandstone used as corner blocks in the Gatehouse, Goblin Tower and elsewhere, may be from the Carboniferous Basement Beds of Pont Lawnt ; sometimes the colour changes to a purplish hue in different parts of the same block. As far as can be seen, all the building materials of the castle and town-wall can be matched among these local rocks.

CHAPTER V

THE WELSH STONE CASTLES

Besides the early stone castles so far described there are others, mostly situated on small rocky hill-tops in the less accessible parts of North Wales, which are ascribed to Welsh builders. Two of them, namely Dolwyddelan and Dolbadarn, are built on the early English plan and consist simply of a keep and bailey. Others are essentially different in plan from the English strongholds. They are especially distinguished by the apsidal form of the principal tower, the inner half being square or oblong with a semicircular end projecting outwards. Usually this tower is placed at one end and connected by curtain-walls with a round tower at the other end of the site. This is the case at Elwoe and Carndochan but at Dinas Bran the apsidal tower is in the centre of a long curtain wall and at Criccieth there are two such towers one on either side of the gateway while the subsidiary towers are rectangular. The site is often surrounded partially or wholly by a ditch cut in the rock, projecting masses being left to support a timber bridge where such a structure is necessary.

DOLWYDDELAN CASTLE
> 6 in. Ordnance map. Caernarvonshire 23 S.W.
> Geological map. WILLIAMS and BULMAN. 1931.
> Architecture and History. RADFORD. 1934.

Though the mediaeval castle is of simple plan it is ascribed to three periods of construction. The rectangular keep, of Norman type, may have been built in the latter half of the 12th century and was presumably surrounded by a courtyard enclosed by a timber stockade. The latter was replaced early in the 13th century by a stone curtain-wall, and the defences were finally completed later in the century by the erection of a second tower in the north-west angle of the courtyard. The upper floor and battlements of the keep were added in the 19th century.

The castle stands on a small knoll, 700 ft. above O.D., forming part of a steep ridge which extends almost east and west and roughly parallel with the valley of the Lledr some 500 ft. below. The ridge is formed of volcanic tuff that dips 40° N.N.W. A second ridge of the same rock lies about 200 yards to the south, the intervening ground being occupied by black, cleaved shales. Proceeding from these central shales, rhyolitic volcanic tuff, shale, a lower tuff and another shale appear in succession both northward and southward. The central shale has proved to be

31

the youngest of the series, and the structure is therefore a syncline. It has, however, been compressed and thrust over from the south-east so that the dip is consistently to the N.W. The general structure of the area was established by Sir A. C. RAMSAY and his assistants on the Geological Survey eighty years ago, but recently H. WILLIAMS and O. M. B. BULMAN have added further details to our knowledge of the syncline. The general distribution of the rocks near the castle is shown on the accompanying map (Fig. 11).

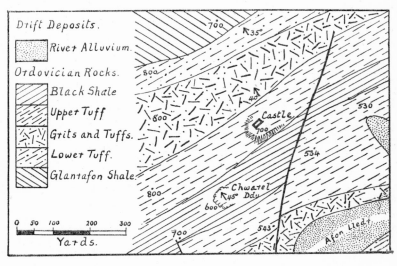

FIG. 11.   Geological Sketch-map of Dolwyddelan Castle
(based on Williams and Bulman, 1931)

The ground rises on either side of the central shale owing to the more resistant nature of the volcanic rocks, and thus the inner rim of the syncline has provided a site for the castle. The steep sides of the ridge need no modification for defence but the site has been artificially isolated on the east and west by ditches cut across the ridge.

The source of water supply is somewhat uncertain as no well has yet been discovered. An adequate supply would be expected on the site for numerous springs at the junction of rhyolite and shale were active in the dry summer of 1934, and the annual rainfall is high.

The masonry is almost entirely of local material, laid irregularly ; the larger blocks of rhyolitic tuff are roughly dressed on one face which is placed externally, the irregular inner spaces

32

being partially filled with small pieces of highly cleaved black shale. Sometimes larger pieces of the shale are interspersed with the blocks of tuff and are laid with the cleavage planes horizontal. The tuff is obtainable actually on the castle site, and a large quarry (Chwarel ddu) in the black shales lies a short distance south-west of the castle.

The arches of the main doorway and the windows in the keep, also of those in the West Tower, are made of slabs of shale set with the cleavage planes normal to the curve of the arch and keyed with a thicker slab worked into a wedge-like shape. In the West Tower the keystone is a wedge-like slab of tuff. The arches therefore show an excellent adaptation of rough intractable material, a feature often seen in Welsh buildings (Fig. 21).

The south window and bases of the doorway in the West Tower are made of hard, white or red-stained sandstone. This is not a local stone, but it seems to be similar to the sandstone used for floor arches at Conway Castle, which most likely came from the Chester district (see p. 45).

DOLBADARN CASTLE

6 in. Ordnance map.   Caernarvonshire 16 N.E.
1 in. Geological map.   Old Series, Sheet 78 N.E.

This castle stands on a lofty spur between Llyn Padarn and Llyn Peris, overlooking a strip of alluvium which has accumulated at the S.E. end of Llyn Padarn. It commands the lower end of the route to the Snowdon country through the magnificent glacial valley which forms the Pass of Llanberis. The ruins consist of a round keep (with an inside diameter of 26 feet) and a few fragments of walls (Fig. 8).

The site lies in the Slate Belt of the Cambrian System which continues from the north through the Dinorwic Slate quarries (north of the lakes) to a short distance south of the castle where the slates are replaced in the same line of strike by grits and conglomerates of the same system ; the east to west junction is faulted, according to the Geological Survey map, and the outcrop of the grits is repeated by several meridional faults. " It is the complication of these faults that apparently gives the upper Cambrian grit an undue importance along the Southern shores of the lakes. Forming a mass of rugged hills and broken ground, they appear far thicker than they actually are." (RAMSAY 1866). Unfortunately the later maps of Snowdon (H. WILLIAMS 1927) and Nant Peris (D. WILLIAMS 1930) both end just short of the castle site.

The interior of the keep is blocked with debris and nothing can be said of the presence of a well. The water supply is probably not copious in the slate or grit outcrop, but the lakes are within a short distance.

The castle is built mainly of fair-sized blocks of purple and green slate, but blocks of grit and fine-grained rocks (some glacial boulders) are interspersed in the masonry. A window-sill and some window-tops are made of thick slabs of slate, but a few of the window-arches are formed of thin wedges of slate placed with the cleavage-surface normal to the curve of the arch as at Dolwyddelan. The masonry is placed directly on the outcrop of the solid rock ; there is no obvious cut for a foundation.

EWLOE CASTLE

6 in. Ordnance map. Flintshire 10 S.W.
1 in. Geological map. New Series, Sheet 108.
Architecture and History. Flintshire Inventory 1912. HEMP. 1928.

The castle of Ewloe, on the eastern boundary of the Principality of Wales, owes its political and strategical importance to its situation on the flank of the coastal route from Chester into Gwynedd. The present castle, built by Prince Llewelyn in 1256-7, is described by HEMP as purely Welsh in plan. It has two towers at the eastern and western ends of the connecting curtain walls, the eastern one of apsidal form and enclosed in an upper ward.

The site is about one mile from the shore of the Dee estuary, at the confluence of the Wepre Brook and its chief tributary (now known as the New Inn brook). The ravines occupied by the streams respectively form the north-western and north-eastern limits of the site. The hill between the ravines is capped by a sandstone of the Coal Measures which dips to the S.S.E. at an angle of 50°, while the streams cut into the underlying shales of the Middle Coal Measures. East of the castle the hill is truncated by a meridional fault which brings shales into juxtaposition with the sandstone. The 200 ft. contour line passes just below the castle on the north, and the ground rises to south and south-west where the site has been isolated by a great ditch. Outside the ravines the solid rocks are largely concealed by Glacial deposits (map, Fig. 12).

The well (now restored) in the lower ward is supplied by a spring at the junction of the sandstone and shale. Owing to the friable nature of the shales, the four sides of the well had to be supported by timbers.

The towers and the curtain walls are built almost entirely of a yellowish sandstone, evidently obtained from the local outcrops of the Coal Measures. The massive Ewloe Castle rock, exposed for some distance up the dingle of Altami Brook, may be equivalent to the Connah's Quay Sandstone, i.e., the sandstone below the Premier Coal (see p. 11). The largest blocks, roughly dressed on the external face, are used in the corner work. The

Fig. 13. Dolbadarn Castle, guarding the Pass of Llanberis. (*Photo Judges*)

Fig. 14. Deganwy Castle, view of site from the western bank of the
Conway Estuary. (*Photo E.N.*)

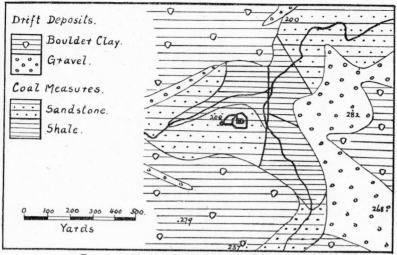

FIG. 12. Geological Sketch-map of Ewloe Castle
(*based on Geol. Surv., New Series, 108*)

infilling of rubble includes some rounded boulders of the same stone but no foreign boulders are apparent. A worked sandstone used in window casings is softer and coarser, and is perhaps from the same locality as a reddish sandstone which forms the bases of door jambs. This is probably from a quarry yielding white and reddish sandstone on the east side of the dingle 130 yards below the junction of the streams. Here 25 ft. of sandstone overlies purple shale, and further sandstone has been proved by boring (WEDD & KING 1924) ; the top sandstone is assigned to the horizon of the Hollin Rock (see p. 10). The mortar contains shells of *Cardium* and *Tellina ;* hence it is made of shore sand probably brought from the Dee estuary.

DEGANWY CASTLE

      6 in. Ordnance map. Caernarvonshire 4 N.E.
      Geological map. ELLES. 1909.
      Architecture and History. LOWE. 1912.

According to historical records, several castles (presumably of wood) were successively built at Deganwy, before the stone castle represented by the existing ruins was erected in 1210-11. HEMP (1928) cites Deganwy as a castle which, like Ewloe and others, shows features of a distinctive Welsh plan.

The ruins occupy two small hills, about 350 ft. above sea-level, which rise abruptly from flat ground just above the 200 ft. contour line (Fig. 14). The hills are connected by artificial

35

earthworks and the space between them formed a central court-yard which would be untenable without possession of both hills. A plan of the foundations is given in Lowe 1912.

The hills are formed of fine-grained (but sometimes brecciated and nodular), creamy-coloured volcanic rocks of the Ordovician System known as rhyolite, which dip generally south-eastward at about 30°. By reason of their hardness they weather less readily than the contiguous rocks and so stand out in bold relief. The condition of softer material mingled with black shale on the western slope of the eastern hill suggests some disturbance (in the geological sense) which would explain the existence of the hollow between the two hills. The site is isolated on the north by a fault which throws down to the north and displaces the rocks westwards (see ELLES 1909). A line of low hills, some 100 yds. south of the castle, formed of the same rhyolite separates the site from low ground occupied by shales.

Little information is available concerning water supply. There are wells at present in the low ground south of the castle, but the site itself furnishes no evidence of water, not even in the central hollow. Lowe (1912) suggests that the large excavation on the western hill, 14 yards square and 20 feet deep, formed a reservoir. This seems improbable ; it may have been made in order to obtain stone for internal repairs.

The building-stone is almost entirely the rhyolite which forms the hills. The sides of the hills are cut away to form sheer slopes, and the stone doubtless was used for building the walls. The bedded rhyolite is often seen in useful blocks, more or less rectangular, presumably fractured along natural joints. The best blocks were used for outside walls ; good surfaces are still seen on the north side of the ruins and on the southern wall of the central court where a junction is made with the natural outcrop. The irregular shape of most blocks, which are intractable and hard to dress, makes necessary a large quantity of mortar. This contains shells of *Cardium* and *Mytilus*, as well as rounded pebbles (including fragments of shale) and was most likely provided by the shore sand of the Conway estuary. Two glacial boulders (probably of dolerite) are noted in the walls of the northern group of buildings.

DINAS BRAN

   6 in. Ordnance map. Denbighshire 34 S.E.
   1 in. Geological map. New Series, Sheet 121.
   Architecture and History. Denbighshire Inventory 1914.

The existing castle was built about 1270 within an old British encampment (ELLIS DAVIES 1929). The main tower, of apsidal shape, faces the southern slope of the site.

FIG. 15. Castell Dinas Bran, view from the east showing the form of the site.

(Photo Valentine)

FIG. 16. Criccieth Castle viewed from the east.   *(Photo Judges)*

The site is a hill, roughly conical in shape and some 1062 ft. high, which commands the valley of the Dee some 500 ft. below. The hill is formed of mudstones and shales assigned, on the evidence of fossils, to the Lower Ludlow Series of the Silurian System. The rocks dip southward at about 25°, and the dip determines the slope of the hill southwards to the river Dee. The northern slope is steep (about 45°) and is determined by the dip of cleavage-planes which have developed as a result of pressure due to earth-movement (Fig. 15). The hill is limited on the north by a fault which brings the much younger Carboniferous rocks into juxtaposition with the Silurian at about 700 ft. above sea-level. The low ground, occupied by red marls and sandstones, is succeeded northwards by a great escarpment of Carboniferous Limestone, which is breached at rare intervals by steep valleys.

On the south and east of the castle-site is a quarry-like ditch cut in the solid rock, and a well is to be seen in the south-east corner of the ditch. According to the Denbighshire Inventory (p. 121) the original well of the castle is inside the castle at the eastern end. Water from this well is used at the present day for the needs of a refreshment hut and the supply was maintained even during the dry summers of 1933 and 1934. The hill is traversed by numerous joints which allow a high degree of percolation of rain water, and as the rainfall is high the water-supply is constant.

The castle is built of the mudstone which forms the site, and the great ditch was probably the source of supply. The stone is intractable material for building owing to its cleavage and this probably accounts for the rough character of the walls. Hence these are not necessarily of early construction as some writers have supposed.

CARNDOCHAN CASTLE

6 in. Ordnance map.   Merioneth 21 S.E.
1 in. Geological map.   Old Series 74 S.W.
Architecture and History.   Merioneth Inventory 1921.

This castle, built in the 13th or 14th century, has an oblong tower rounded at the S.W. end, and a square tower to the N.E. of the site. The ruins are situated on a spur of the Arenig mountains known as Moel y Graig which ends abruptly in a craggy promontory jutting out into the alluvial plain of the Afon Lliw, about 1½ miles west of Llanuwchllyn at the S.W. end of Bala Lake. The site is just above the 1000 ft. contour-line and it lies 400 ft. above the valley floor ; it is isolated by precipitous slopes, except on the S.W. where a low col connects it with the higher ground of Moel y Graig and Graig y Llestri (1500 ft.).

The rock is a massive, obscurely-bedded tuff which dips approximately eastward at about 50°, and weathers almost like a massive grit. The area has not been surveyed recently but it appears to be an extension of the Arenig country to the north described by FEARNSIDES (1905) who assigns similar rocks to the Llandeilo Series of the Ordovician System. The Castle crags seem to correspond with his Middle Series, while the lower slopes to the east are probably formed of his Upper Series. The col to the S.W. of the site is probably formed by a strip of the Upper tuffs let down between two faults (Geol. Surv. Map, Old Series 74 S.W.). North-east of the site, black shales are exposed in the lower ground, with a covering of Boulder Clay in places.

A ditch is cut in front of the castle facing the col. At the northern end of the ditch is a spring which is probably connected with the faults mentioned above ; there is also marshy ground a little further west. This seems the most likely course of the water-supply.

The walls, best seen in the south-western apsidal tower, are built of the tuff exposed on the site. Blocks are dressed on one side for facing of the walls ; some rounded blocks are probably glacial boulders. Interstices in the walling are filled with smaller pieces of tuff and mortar. The latter contains small pebbles (including black shale), waterworn and similar to gravel in the valley of the stream below the castle. Included in the mortar there are also pieces of Carboniferous Limestone, some of which are imperfectly burned, and still show traces of fossils. The nearest outcrop of Carboniferous Limestone is 14 miles away to the north-east at Hafod y Calch near Corwen, and it seems reasonable to suppose that lime for making mortar was obtained from this source.

CRICCIETH CASTLE

6 in. Ordnance map. Caernarvonshire 34 S.W.
1 in. Geological map. Old Series, Sheet 75 S.W.
Architecture and History. O'NEIL. 1944.

This castle, probably the work of Welsh builders (O'NEIL 1934 ; 1944), and afterwards adapted by Edward I, stands on a rounded hill which juts far out into the sea (Fig. 16). The hill, just over 100 ft. high, is formed of a cream or pink-coloured igneous rock known as felsite. It is continuous with the rock of Dinas to the north-west which is closely similar but shows columnar jointing in places. This mass of igneous rock is generally assigned to the Ordovician System but it may be a later intrusion ; its precise relation to the Ordovician shale of the district is concealed by a covering of Boulder Clay.

A compact igneous rock such as felsite would hardly be expected to yield a copious supply of water. On the castle site, however, the rock is highly jointed ; consequently percolation of rain-water into the body of the hill is possible and the water may gradually collect, by intricate routes, at certain places which are difficult to detect from the surface. Remains of a well have been discovered (O'NEIL 1944) in the eastern side of the entrance passage of the gatehouse, and it is likely that a spring was located there during or after the building of the castle, for, as O'NEIL points out, the well would otherwise not be constructed in such an awkward position.

The felsite is the main building material of the castle ; blocks are placed with a smooth face to the exterior of the wall, while the irregular sides are fixed in the rubble filling. Otherwise the castle is remarkable for the large number of rounded boulders in the walls—probably obtained locally from the Glacial Drift. Some are large ; for instance a broken boulder of coarse dolerite in the wall of the west tower is 3 ft. across, large flat boulders of dolerite are among the felsite blocks at the S.E. corner of the gatehouse, another (measuring about 4 ft. by 2 ft. by 2 ft.) supports a corner in the wall west of the gatehouse. As the edges of the boulders are rounded, the joints in the walling are wide ; these are partly filled with smaller pieces of rock, including black cleaved shale which can be matched at various places within a mile of the castle. The shale is also utilised in the casing of loopholes in the front of the gatehouse, also in window-arches when the slabs are placed with their cleavage-planes normal to the curve of the arch, the keystone being a wedge-shaped slab of the same rock. Some loop casings, however, are made of the felsite. While most of the building material is of local origin, some of the stone used in various parts of the castle is certainly foreign to the district. For example, some corner-stones in the entrance to the gatehouse are of coarse pebbly sandstone which can be matched among the Carboniferous rocks of eastern Anglesey. Other sandstones are noted in the western tower, and some loose worked blocks of buff-coloured sandstone displayed in the outer ward probably come from the same source ; they may include the " querns of Anglesey grit " mentioned by O'NEIL (1944). All these rocks remind one of the sandstone material used in Beaumaris Castle during the last few years of the 13th century (see page 50).

Chapter VI

THE CASTLES OF EDWARD I

The method carried out by Edward I for controlling North Wales was very different from that of his predecessors. He erected a series of castles at intervals around the coast, and relied largely on the sea-passage from his base at Chester to maintain communication between them. By this means North Wales as a whole was cut off from the " granary " of Anglesey which had enabled the Welsh tribesmen to hold out against former invaders.

During the 13th century the design of castles developed into the so-called " concentric " type with curtain walls and bastion towers. But in North Wales the choice of site was limited by the necessity for providing harbourage for shipping, and consequently symmetry of design often had to be sacrificed in order to accommodate the building to the site. At the same time, the use of sea-transport made possible a wider range in the choice of building material, and the masons were no longer hampered by the limitations of local sources of supply.

It is convenient to describe this series of castles from east to west along the coast, and it happens that this is approximately the chronological order of building. Nearest to the base at Chester, some 12 miles distant, is the Castle of Flint (1277-80) which also commanded the estuary of the Dee. Some fifteen miles further west is Rhuddlan Castle (1281-91) with a convenient harbour in the mouth of the River Clwyd. The massive Castle of Conway (1284-1302), overlooks the estuary of the River Conway, and the magnificent pile of Caernarvon (1285-1322), commanding the western entrance to Menai Strait, had ample harbourage for the ships of the period in the mouth of the River Saint. The Castle of Harlech (1285-90) formerly had a landing place at the foot of its rocky site, but the wide Morfa has since been deposited on its seaward side. The Castle of Beaumaris (1295-98), built after the Welsh rising of 1294, commands the eastern entrance to the Menai Strait and also formed a bridgehead on the isle of Anglesey.

FLINT CASTLE

6 in. Ordnance map. Flintshire 6q N.E.

1 in. Geological map. New Series, Sheet 108.

Architecture and History. Flintshire Inventory 1912. HEMP. 1929.

As is usual in the fortifications built by Edward I in North
Wales the town and castle of Flint were designed as a single
defensive unit.   The castle is built on a small outcrop of sandstone belonging to the Middle Coal Measures which projects
through the covering of Drift deposits and abuts on the Dee
estuary.   Yellowish shaly sandstone is seen at the base of the
N.E. and N.W. towers, the rock under the N.E. tower being
undercut and filled in with masonry.   No rock is visible under
the curtain walls and southern towers, and the S.E. bastion
forms a separate donjon.   On the south of the site the Boulder
Clay rises to slightly above site-level and the shores to east and
west are marshy.

Water is provided by two wells, one in the Great Tower
and one in the Inner Bailey.   The surface of the latter is higher
than the floor of the lower storey in the tower; allowing for this,
the water level in the two wells appear to be the same.   Judging
by the size of the outcrop, and the difficulties in the modern
water-supply of the town, the yield of the wells is likely to have
been scanty, and the water is liable to become brackish by
infiltration from the estuary.

The main building material in the castle walls is a yellowish
sandstone from the Coal Measures ; it is probably the stone,
nor far below the Premier Coal (see Fig. 4), seen in quarries
within a mile or two S.E. of the castle.   The ashlar facings are
properly laid with the bedding horizontal, but all the stone is
now much weathered, especially the more shaly material which
is less resistant.   A red sandstone containing small pebbles is
used as ashlar in parts of the west wall and the Great Tower,
also as rubble-filling indiscriminately.   This stone resembles
the Middle Bunter Sandstone of Wirral and Chester, and was
probably brought from the latter locality.   Boulders from the
Drift also appear as rubble in the revetment on the inner side of
the moat.   The mortar contains shells of *Tellina* and *Cardium* ;
hence fine shingle was probably obtained from the adjacent
shore.   The major proportion of the building material was
therefore obtained from local sources, but some red sandstone
was probably transported from the neighbourhood of Chester.

RHUDDLAN CASTLE

6 in. Ordnance map. Flintshire 4 N.E.
1 in. Geological map. Old Series 79 N.W.
Architecture and History. Flintshire Inventory 1912.

The existing ruins of Edward I's castle (1281-91) form a simple quadrangle, with single round towers (42 feet in height) at the north and south, and double towers of the same height at the east and west corners. The curtain walls, some 35 ft. high, enclose a courtyard 48 yards by 43 yards, and contain sockets for the timbers of lean-to buildings. The outer ward, added a few years later, is enclosed by a river-wall with a small square tower, and by a moat lined with masonry on the side remote from the river. The castle stands on a ridge of Boulder Clay at about 50 feet above O.D. ; a boring near Plas Newydd just south of the site proved this deposit to be more than 32 feet. in thickness (STRAHAN 1885). The site commands the River Clwyd and the adjacent outlet to the sea, while to the west is the Morfa Rhuddlan formed by the silting up of the wide estuary (Fig. 17).

A well in the centre of the courtyard contains water at a depth of about 50 ft., that is, practically at river-level. This may have been supplied by seepage through the Glacial deposits which in this neighbourhood often include lenticles of sand, but, as the River Clwyd is tidal up to Rhuddlan, there must have been a risk of infiltration of brackish water from the estuary.

No stone is available in the immediate vicinity of the castle, except boulders contained in the Glacial deposits, and these are not suitable for good masonry ; they are, however, used sparingly in the rubble-filling between the ashlar facings of the walls.

Four distinct varieties of building-stone are evident in the ruins and their source can be stated with some approach to accuracy. The curtain-walls and the revetment wall of the ditch are built mainly of grey Carboniferous Limestone ; the irregular sides being fixed in the rubble-filling. This stone may well have been brought from the northern end of Moel Hiraddug, Dyserth, 2 miles away ; the various localities on the western side of the Vale of Clwyd are less likely sources. Large squared blocks of a distinctive Purple Sandstone are used in the lower courses of the towers, both externally and internally, sometimes alternating with blocks of grey limestone. Little mortar is used with this purple rock, for it is a freestone and has been accurately squared ; it is also used for steps of the lower stair in the eastern double tower. The only visible source for this stone is an old quarry on the River Elwy, two miles S.S.W. of St. Asaph, and some 300 yards west of Pont yr allt goch. (NEAVERSON 1946).

Fig. 17. Rhuddlan Castle, view from the north-west. (*Photo Valentine*)

Fig. 18. Harlech Castle viewed from the north. (*Photo Judges*)

Another sandstone, of bright red colour, is of Triassic age ; it is used in smaller blocks for corner and morticed work in the curtain walls, for arches in the inner wall of the curtain, and for window-frames, including those of the small river-tower. The stone is evenly grained, sometimes current-bedded, with no pebbles ; it may have been brought, probably by sea, from the neighbourhood of Chester. The upper courses of the towers are made of a yellowish or buff sandstone like that used in Flint Castle ; in the north tower it is set alternatively with limestone. The stone is often thin-bedded rather than massive, and in this form is used for stairways in the eastern double tower, and for lintels of doorways, as on the western side of the north tower. This sandstone of the Coal Measures was probably brought to Rhuddlan from the neighbourhood of Flint.

We may note that the walls of the river-tower contain building stones of three kinds, Carboniferous Limestone, Coal Measures sandstone, and red Triassic sandstone, similar to those of the curtain walls and towers save that the last-named have purple sandstone in addition. Therefore the river-tower was almost certainly built at the same period as the Castle itself, and is not Norman as claimed by W. B. Lowe (1927).

CONWAY CASTLE

    6 in. Ordnance map. Caernarvonshire 4 S.E.
    Geological map. G. L. ELLES. 1909.
    Architecture and History. CLARK. 1884.

According to T. H. CLARK (1884) the town and castle of Conway together form the most complete and best preserved example of mediaeval military architecture in Britain. Begun in 1285 and finished by 1302, it functioned as a bridgehead to cover the passage of the River Conway.

The walled town, with the castle at its south-eastern angle, stands on a ridge trending roughly east and west from the western bank of the Conway estuary and along the northern bank of its tributary, the Afon Gyffin. The ridge is composed mainly of strong grits or sandstones of the Silurian System which stand out from the contiguous Ordovician mudstones by reason of their superior hardness ; the beds are inclined to the south at an angle of about 50°, and this high dip accounts for the narrow outcrop of the grit. West of the church the beds are faulted, so that the grit is displaced some 40 or 50 yards southwards, a displacement which is reflected in the curved form of the town wall. Another fault with a similar N.W. to S.E. trend occurs just west of the western angle of the wall which is 125 feet above O.D. This fault throws the grit much farther southwards and brings flat shaly ground into juxtaposition with the grit ridge of the town. The grit is underlaid northwards by shales and mudstones which weather uniformly ; consequently the northern wall is straight. Still further north, the town is dominated by the much larger ridge of Conway Mountain which extends westwards from the shore at Bodlondeb ; this ridge is composed of an igneous rock called rhyolite, which offers greater resistance to the weathering agents than do the sedimentary rocks beneath the town. These features are shown in the sketch-map (Fig. 19).

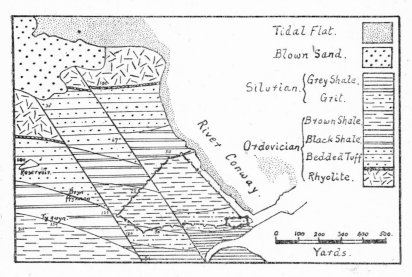

FIG. 19. Geological Sketch-map of Conway Castle and walled town
(*based on Elles, 1909*)

The Castle is built at the eastern end of the grit ridge, in the angle between the Conway estuary and its tributary, the Afon Gyffin. The ridge is said to have formerly projected further east as far as the rock which forms the western foundation of the modern bridges ; it is there cut off by the strong fault-line occupied by the Conway estuary, but reappears on the other side of the river south of Deganwy, having been displaced some 800 yards to the north. Obviously, the castle site does not favour the concentric plan fashionable in the 13th century ; the castle is elongated in the direction of the ridge, and there is no elaborate gateway.

44

Water-supply. The Silurian grit lying above impermeable Ordovician shales might be expected to act as a storage for underground water, but at Conway the dip of the rock is so steep, and the outcrop so narrow that the supply would be extremely limited. In the larger court of the castle there is a reservoir 15 feet in diameter and 20 feet in depth. CLARK (1884) states that it was lined and cemented for the storage of water which was brought into it from the roofs and from a spring outside the castle. According to LOWE (1912) the external source was a well above Ty Gwyn, and there is a tradition that the pipe-line was once cut by the enemy and the garrison forced to surrender. It may be added that the run-off of surface water from the slopes of Conway Mountain is considerable and there is a modern reservoir above Tygwyn Cottages, a short distance west of the walls ; again, the field name Brynffynnon nearby suggests the site of a spring or well. These features are apparently near the traditional location for the site of the well which supplied the castle.

Building-stone. The walls of the castle are built entirely of the hard Silurian grit that forms the ridge on which the castle stands. There seems little doubt that the stone was obtained near the site, and extensive old quarries still exist immediately S.W. of the town. The southern and western parts of the town-wall are built of the same stone, but the northern and eastern parts of the wall contain much rhyolite, the quay wall being entirely of this rock. LOWE (1912) suggests that this material was brought across the river from the ruins of Deganwy Castle, and it may be that this would involve less labour and expense than quarrying the stone. It should be noted, however, that the same rock forms the whole ridge of Conway Mountain, including the hill at Bodlondeb immediately adjacent to the northern wall. A red and white mottled sandstone is much used for window-casings and mouldings in the Queen's Chapel, for springers of arches in the banquet hall, for hoods and fireplaces in the King's and Queen's towers, and for corbels which support the many lintels of Silurian grit. It is also used in morticed work in the wall of the Queen's Tower, a single shaped block often being used alternately with two separate blocks of grit to form a bond. The source of this stone is commonly supposed to be a quarry at Bodysgallen, 2 miles distant to the N.E. But the Bodysgallen stone has a purple rather than a red colour, and its constituent grains are coarser than those of the red sandstone used in the castle. The latter is much closer in appearance to the Triassic sandstone of the Chester district which must be regarded as the more probable source. Moreover, this opinion is consistent with documentary evidence, for the Black Prince's register, under dates 26th February and 14th March 1347, contains orders for stone to be taken by sea from Chester for repairing the arches of the hall in the castle of Conway. It is reasonable to suppose that the stone for the repairs, only 50 years after the castle was built, would be got from the known original source.

CAERNARVON CASTLE

> 6 in. Ordnance map. Caernarvonshire 15 N.E.
> Geological map. E. GREENLY. 1943.
> Architecture and History. C. R. PEERS. 1917, 1932.

The chief topographical feature of Caernarvon is Twt Hill which forms the southern end of a ridge, over 100 feet in height, trending north-eastwards away from the town. The ridge is composed of a granitic rock which originally was intruded into older rocks and afterwards was exposed by denudation. The remnants of these older rocks (phyllites of Precambrian age) lie beneath the surface, under both the modern and Mediaeval towns of Caernarvon (see map, Fig. 20). They show signs of thermal alteration due to the original heat of the intrusive granite. South-east of Twt Hill a narrow band of Cambrian rocks has been detected by GREENLY (1943), but does not appear further

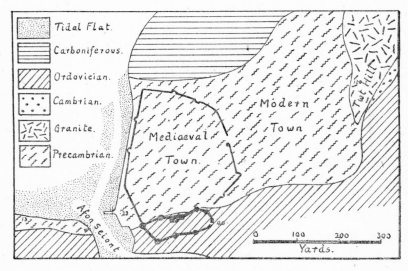

FIG. 20.   Geological Sketch-map of Caernarvon Castle and walled town
(based on Greenly, 1943)

46

west.   North of the walled town the lowlying ground is occupied
by rocks of the Carboniferous System, but these again have no
part in the site under discussion.   The castle stands on a foundation of black Ordovician shales which can be seen under the south-
western walls of the castle ; these shales lie unconformably on
the Precambrian phyllites, and extend southwards from the
Twt Hill and Caernarvon beyond the confines of our area.   In
places the Ordovician rocks seem to be overlaid by Drift deposits,
for the towers and curtain walls on the south and west are said
to be built on " strongly compacted gravel " ; this material is
no longer visible and the walls have been underpinned and
carried down to the rock.   (PEERS 1917).   The shape of the site
does not favour a " concentric " design, but only a single line
of walls forming an irregular quadrangle elongated from west
to east and narrowest in the centre.

The water supply depended largely on the yield of two
wells described by PEERS (1917).   One, in the Inner Court, is
contained in a projection on the east of the well-chamber on
the ground floor, and is sunk about six feet into the shaly rock.
The other, in the Granary Tower is a rectangular shaft which
penetrates about ten feet of the Ordovician shales.   Both are
said to yield excellent water, but apparently the supply was
augmented by rain-water collected from the roofs by a cistern
placed in a turret between the Black Tower and the Queen's
Gate.   On general grounds a water-supply from the impervious
Ordovician shales would appear unpromising, but as the shales
are cleaved and the rainfall is fairly high (up to 60 inches
annually) percolation into the wells may be considerable.
Possibly the water is held up at the junction of the Ordovician
shales and the underlying Precambrian phyllites, and this
junction cannot be at any great depth.

In view of GREENLY's careful work (1932), an account of
the building-stones in the castles of Caernarvon and Beaumaris
may seem superfluous here.   But a summary is desirable in order
to complete our geological review of the Castles.   The principal
building material at Caernarvon is a compact variety of Carboniferous Limestone, and there is little doubt that it was brought
from Penmon in Anglesey.   Next in importance is a Carboniferous sandstone, a light-brown stone often containing pebbles
of quartz ; it is used for ashlar work, wrought and moulded
dressings throughout the castle, also for paving on the upper wall
between the Chamberlain and Black Towers.   This stone
could have come from Penmon where it is associated with the prevalent limestones, but it might have been got from several places
along the Menai Strait, Vaynol Park on the mainland, or Pwllfan-
ogle on the Anglesey side, for example.   A grey grit with dark

knots and films has been used in the interior, especially in the lower parts of the walls. It is much harder than the Carboniferous sandstone, and it has the characters of a grit which lies at the base of the Ordovician shales between Caernarvon and Bangor ; it can be seen in the south-eastern part of the quarry at Twt Hill bach, which may be the " town end quarry " of historical records. A red sandstone, used for springers of arches, for mullions, window-casings and fireplaces, is similar to the Triassic sandstone of Chester ; there is some documentary evidence for the use of this rock in 1347 (P.R.O. 1930-32). Boulders from the glacial deposits are only sparsely used in the building ; a few rocks from Snowdon and a dark green schist from Anglesey have been noted in the interior. Certain blocks of grey granite in the west buttress of the Well Tower are compared by GREENLY with an Irish granite from Newry ; they are said to be ballast used for repairs in the 19th century.

The Town walls, not so well built as the castle are also mainly of Carboniferous Limestone. They contain, however, a larger proportion of sandstone which is mixed irregularly with the limestone. Examination of the pebbles in this sandstone has convinced GREENLY that the stone was obtained from the Vaynol cliffs, west of the Tubular Railway Bridge. Many blocks of red sandstone similar to the Chester rock may be spoil from the Roman ruins of Segontium, as noted by WHEELER (1923).

HARLECH CASTLE

6 in. Ordnance map. Merioneth 19 S.W.
1 in. Geological map. Old Series 75 S.E.
Architecture and History. C. R. PEERS. 1923. PEERS and HEMP. 1934. OMAN. 1926.

The site is a bold and rugged headland, hardly 200 feet above sea-level, overlooking to the west the broad alluvial flat known as the Morfa Harlech. The site has a commanding position though it is overlooked by higher ground to the east. The river Dwyryd, which now joins the estuary of the Glaslyn and flows into the sea near Portmadoc is said to have formerly flowed south-westwards along the edge of the high ground close to the castle rock, reaching the sea a little distance S.W. of the castle. The change of course is probably due to silting up with tidal alluvium on the southern side of the estuary. The castle rock is a spur of the Harlech Dome, a famous feature of geological structure. The rock is a hard tough grit or sandstone belonging to the lower part of the Cambrian System. The castle is isolated from the high ground to the east by a broad deep ditch quarried in the rock ; it is debatable if this ditch was ever intended to hold water.

Water-supply for the castle was obtained from a well which partly underlies the north curtain of the inner ward in the north-eastern angle of the court. The presence of water on the site is probably due to the heavily-jointed character of the rock which facilitates percolation of the rainfall to a considerable degree. The water-level in the well in the dry summer of 1935 was estimated at about ten feet below ground-level.

The walls and towers are built mainly of the Harlech Grit quarried in the vicinity of the castle; indeed, outcrops of the rock are seen immediately under the walls in the middle and outer wards. It is a hard grey sandstone or grit whose constituent grains are cemented by siliceous material; it varies considerably in texture, some blocks containing many pebbles, being almost conglomeratic. Some of the sandstone blocks in the walls appear to be glacial boulders, for they are smoothed and rounded; some are sufficiently flat and tabular for use without squaring, others have been split to give a flat surface for the outer face of the wall. The grit has also been used in the fireplace of the Great Hall and in the south-western corner of the kitchen where a fireplace may have been; blocks worked as quadrants appear also in the oven of the Great Hall. In these examples the stone has been burned to a red colour, similar to that shown where bonfires have been lighted on the rock of Twt Hill a short distance south of the castle.

Slabs of slate are sometimes interspersed with the grit masonry and smaller pieces of slate are often seen in the interstices between the larger blocks. Both rocks are used, in slabs up to eight inches thick, for steps of stairs and for flat lintels to doorways; slate wedges are also used in the construction of arches. The slate is certainly of local origin, for it is occasionally interbedded in the Harlech Grit Series, and is dominant in the famous Cambrian Slates of Llanberis and Bethesda.

The window-frames are made generally of a soft yellowish sandstone which has yielded to weathering much more readily than the Harlech Grit of the walls. The same sandstone is also used for door-lintels and sometimes for corner blocks in the masonry; the hoods of fireplaces in the gate-house (not accessible) seem from a distance to be of the same material. The rock bears close resemblance to some of the Carboniferous sandstones of Anglesey; it is a freestone which contains grains of quartz three or four millimetres in diameter interspersed among the smaller grains, and ashlar blocks of this stone require very little mortar.

The aggregate of the mortar is a shore sand with rounded fragments of quartz, grit and shale together with broken shells of *Tellina*, cockle and mussel.

BEAUMARIS CASTLE

6 in. Ordnance map. Anglesey 15 S.W.
1 in. Geological map. Anglesey Special Sheet (Geol. Surv.).
Architecture and History. BAYNES. 1927. HEMP. 1933. Anglesey
    Inventory. 1937.

This castle is often cited as an example of a purely concentric fortress in which the architect was free to design his work without being hampered by irregularities of the ground. It is built on a marshy flat close to the seashore, and only slightly above the level of the sea from which its ditch was filled. The site is floored by Boulder Clay of which the depth is unknown, but cliff-sections on the coast show 30 to 40 feet of the deposit, and a compound drumlin 50 feet in height is cut through by the sea not far from the castle. The Boulder Clay is reddish in colour, and the smoothed and striated boulders are chiefly Carboniferous Limestone, presumably transported by the ice from the outcrop in the Penmon area some miles to the north.

Little can be said regarding the water-supply of the castle. Small supplies of water are sometimes obtained from sandy lenticles in the Boulder Clay, and the six-inch map shows two wells in the Drift area not far from the castle. Hence the castle may have been supplied by a well within its walls, but the position of such a well is uncertain. Moreover, in view of the close proximity to the sea, there would always be the risk of sea-water percolating into the well.

The several types of building material used in the castle have been described by E. GREENLY (1932), and have been examined independently by the writer. Carboniferous Limestone is probably the most widely used ; some is excellent stone, but much of it is laminated and shaly, and therefore inferior as building material. It is sometimes said to have come from Penmon but GREENLY thinks the cliffs about a mile north of Benllech a more likely source, and this may be the " quarry five leagues distant " mentioned in the old records. A more compact limestone seems to have been used for the vault and arcade in the chapel. Not all the limestone is quarried material ; some glacial boulders are to be seen at the top of the S.W. Tower, and in the same place is a block riddled with annelid borings and evidently picked up on the shore.

A pebbly sandstone is also widely used, especially for corner work where large squared blocks are necessary, as in the entrance gate for instance. It is also used for lintels of doorways (Fig. 22) and window-casings throughout the castle, for mouldings and arches along the inner curtain wall, for floor-arches across towers, and for steps in the stairs from the chapel to the top of the walls. It is an even-grained sandstone containing pebbles of quartz ;

FIG. 21.　Dolwyddelan Castle ; doorway in West Tower
with arch of cleaved slate.　　(*Photo E.N.*)

FIG. 22.　Beaumaris Castle ; doorway in Northern block
with lintel of pebbly sandstone.　　(*Photo E.N.*)

it is not hard to work but is unsuitable for fine carving, so the decoration of the castle is simple. From a study of the records KNOOP and JONES (1933) locate the source of the sandstone as near Vaynol on the mainland. GREENLY, however, who knows the rocks intimately, states definitely that it is not from Vaynol or the Straits area, but may easily have come from Penmon where sandstones are associated with the Carboniferous Limestone. We may also note, with GREENLY, that the proportion of sandstone over limestone is much greater at Beaumaris than at Caernarvon.

Perhaps the most distinctive rocks of Anglesey are the Precambrian green schists, laminated metamorphic rocks which are usually intensely corrugated. They are intractable as building material, nevertheless they appear in some quantity in the lower courses of the curtain walls, but are rarely seen above the height of about ten feet. Certain peculiarities in the rock, such as the inosculation of limestone in some blocks of the schist, lead GREENLY to cite Pen y parc as a likely source ; this is only $1\frac{1}{2}$ miles away to the south-west, at an elevation of 300 feet so that transport to the castle would be all downhill. Near by is a long volcanic dyke which probably furnished the blocks of black dolerite that appear here and there in the curtain walls.

Apart from these local rocks which form the bulk of the building material, there are only some small slabs of purple slate and a few pieces of rhyolite which may be glacial erratics transported by ice from the Snowdon district. A block of red sandstone, noted at the south end of the Gunner's Walk, may be a fortuitous addition from Chester.

From the foregoing review, certain general conclusions emerge concerning the geological setting of the mediaeval castles in North Wales. The position of the mounds for the Norman strongholds seems to depend as much on the character of the geological substratum as on strategical considerations. The sites of the stone castles are seen to have been moulded by a diversity of geological processes operating through vast periods of time. The characters and relations of the rocks underlying these sites have determined both the nature of the water-supply and the occurrence of suitable building material. In those cases where building-stones have been transported from a distance, historical records are usually vague concerning the source of supply, and the provenance can only be determined by a detailed examination of the materials themselves. Hence there is much to be gained by a full co-operation between archaeologists and geologists ; this view was staunchly supported by W. L. HOBBS to whom this work is dedicated.

APPENDIX

References to Literature cited in the Text.

ARMITAGE, E. S. 1912. The early Norman Castles of the British Isles.

BAYNES, E. N. 1927. The Early History of Beaumaris Castle. *Trans. Anglesey Antiq. Soc.*, pp. 49-61.

CLARK, T. H. 1884. Mediaeval Military Architecture.

COX, E. W. 1895. Chester Castle. *Journ. Chester Arch. Soc.*, vol. v, pp. 239-276.

DAVIES, E. 1929. Prehistoric and Roman Remains of Denbighshire.

EDWARDS, T. 1912. Dyserth Castle. *Arch. Camb.*, vol. xii, pp. 263-294.

ELLES, G. L. 1909. The Relations of the Ordovician and Silurian Rocks of Conway. *Quart. Journ. Geol. Soc.*, vol. lxv, pp. 169-194.

FEARNSIDES, W. G. 1905. The Geology of Arenig Fawr and Moel Llyfrnant. *Quart. Journ. Geol. Soc.*, vol. lxxvii, pp. 608-640.

FEARNSIDES, W. G. 1910. The Tremadoc Slates of S.E. Caernarvonshire. *Quart. Journ. Geol. Soc.*, vol. lxvi, pp. 142-188.

GREENLY, E. 1932. The Stones of the Castles [Beaumaris and Caernarvon]. *Trans. Anglesey Antiq. Soc.*, pp. 50-56.

GREENLY, E. 1943. The Older Rocks of Caernarvon. *Proc. Liverpool Geol. Soc.*, vol. xviii, pp. 113-119.

HEMP, W. J. 1926. Denbigh Castle. Official Guide. H.M. Office of Works.

HEMP, W. J. 1926. Denbigh Castle. *Y Cymmrodor*, vol. xxxvi, pp. 65-120.

HEMP, W. J. 1928. The Castle of Ewloe and the Welsh Castle Plan. *Y Cymmrodor*, vol. xxxix, pp. 4-19.

HEMP, W. J. 1929. Ewloe Castle. Official Guide. H.M. Office of Works.

HEMP, W. J. 1929. Flint Castle. Official Guide. H.M. Office of Works.

HEMP, W. J. 1933. Beaumaris Castle. Official Guide. H.M. Office of Works.

HOLME, G. G. 1927. Aber Lleiniog Castle. *In Lowe, W. B.*, 1927, p. 220.

HUGHES, H. H. 1913. Harlech Castle. *Arch. Camb.*

HUGHES, H. H. 1927. Beaumaris Castle. *In Lowe, W. B.*, 1927, pp. 176-181.

JONES, W. GARMON. 1928. The Castles of Wales. *Wonderful Britain*, Amal. Press.

KNOOP, D. and JONES, G. P. 1933. Castle-building at Beaumaris and Caernarvon in the early 14th century. *Ars Quatuor Coronatorium*, vol. xlv.

LLOYD, J. E. 1912. History of Wales from the earliest times to the Edwardian Conquest. 2 vols. London.

LOWE, W. B. 1854. Conway Castle Building Accounts. *Arch. Camb.*, vol. v., pp. 1-12.

LOWE, W. B. 1912-1927. The Heart of Northern Wales. Vol. i, 1912 ; vol. ii, 1927.

NEAVERSON, E. 1930. The Carboniferous rocks around Prestatyn, Dyserth and Newmarket. *Proc. Liverpool Geol. Soc.*, vol. vx, pp. 181-212.

NEAVERSON, E. 1945. The Carboniferous rocks between Abergele and Denbigh. *Proc. Liverpool Geol. Soc.*, vol. xix, pp. 52-68.

NEAVERSON, E. 1946. The Older Building Stones of St. Asaph Cathedral. *Arch. Camb.*, pp. 221-225.

NEWSTEAD, R. 1937. The Roman Station, Prestatyn. First Interim Report, with an appendix on the Geology of the Site by E. NEAVERSON. *Arch. Camb.*, pp. 208-232.

OMAN, C. 1926. Castles. The Great Western Railway.

O'NEIL, B. H., St. J. 1934. Criccieth Castle. Provisional Guide. H.M. Office of Works.

O'NEIL, B. H. St. J. 1944. Criccieth Castle, Caernarvonshire. *Arch. Camb.*, vol. xcviii, pp. 1-51.

PEERS, C. R. 1917. Caernarvon Castle. *Trans. Hon. Soc. Cymmrodorion* (1915-16), pp. 1-74.

PEERS, C. R. 1923. Harlech Castle. *Trans. Soc. Cymmrodorion* (1921-22), pp. 63-82.

PEERS, C. R. 1932. Caernarvon Castle. Official Guide. H.M. Office of Works.

PEERS, C. R. and HEMP, W. J. 1934. Harlech Castle. Official Guide. H.M. Office of Works.

PUBLIC RECORDS OFFICE. 1930-1932. Register of Edward the Black Prince. Part I (1930), 1346-1348 ; Part III (1932), for 1351-1365. *P.R.O. Ancient Correspondence*, vol. lviii, No. 35.

RADFORD, C. A. R. 1934. Dolwyddelan Castle. H.M. Office of Works.

RAMSAY, A. C. 1866. The Geology of North Wales, 2nd Edn. 1881. *Mem. Geol. Surv.*

ROYAL COMMISSION ON ANCIENT AND HISTORICAL MONUMENTS. Inventories. II. The County of Flint, 1912. IV. The County of Denbigh, 1914. Merioneth, 1921. Anglesey, 1937. H.M. Stationery Office.

SHRUBSOLE, G. W. 1887. The Age of the City Walls of Chester. *Arch. Journ.*, vol. xliv, pp. 15-25.

SHRUBSOLE, G. W. 1893. Roman Earthenware Waterpipes in the Grosvenor Museum. *Journ. Chester Arch. Soc.*, vol. v, pp. 28-34.

SHRUBSOLE, G. W. 1893. Great Boughton in the time of the Romans. *Journ. Chester Arch. Soc.*, vol. v, pp. 35-45.

SMITH, B. 1919. The Late Glacial Gravels of the Vale of Edeyrnion, Corwen, N. Wales. *Geol. Mag.*, vol. lvi, pp. 312-318.

STRAHAN, A. 1882. The Geology of the Country around Chester. *Mem. Geol. Survey* (and map, O.S. 80 S.W.).

STRAHAN, A. 1890. The Geology of the neighbourhoods of Flint, Mold and Ruthin. *Mem. Geol. Survey* (and map O.S. 79 S.E.).

WEBB, C. B. and KING, W. B. R. 1924. The Geology of the Country around Flint, Hawarden and Caergwr e. *Mem. Geol. Survey* (and map N.S. 108).

WHEELER, R. E. M. 1923. Segontium and the Roman occupation of Wales. *Y Cymmrodor*, vol. xxxiii.

WILLIAMS, D. 1930. The Geology of the Country between Nant Peris and Nant Ffrancon (Snowdonia). *Quart. Journ. Geol. Soc.*, vol. lxxxvi, pp. 191-233.

WILLIAMS, H. 1927. The Geology of Snowdon (North Wales). *Quart. Journ. Geol. Soc.*, vol. lxxxiii, pp. 346-431.

WILLIAMS, H. and BULMAN, O. M. B. 1931. The Geology of the Dolwyddelan Syncline. *Quart. Journ. Geol. Soc.*, vol. lxxxvii, pp. 425-458.

INDEX

	Page		Page
Aber Lleiniog . .	13, 17	Gwerclas (mound) . . .	21
Alluvium	6	Gwespyr Sandstone . .	11
Aqueduct Grit . . .	12	Gwyddelwern (mound) . .	21
Bala Fault	27	Harlech Castle . .	15, 48
Bala (mound) . . .	21	Harlech Dome . . .	15
Basingwerk Abbey . . .	11	Harlech Grit	15
Beaumaris Castle . .	13, 50	Hawarden Castle . .	12, 25
Beeston Castle . . .	4	Hawarden Mound . . .	17
Blown Sand	6	Hendwr (mound) . . .	21
Boulder Clay . . .	6	Hollin Rock	10
Buckley Fireclay . . .	10	Holt Castle . . .	8, 24
Bunter Sandstone . . .	2	Holywell (mound) . . .	17
Caergwrle Castle . .	12, 27	Holywell Shales . . .	12
Caernarvon Castle . .	13, 46	Keuper Sandstone . . .	5
Cambrian System . . .	15	Llandeilo Series . . .	38
Carboniferous Basement Beds .	30	Llanfor (mound) . . .	21
Carboniferous Limestone . .	12	Llangar (mound) . . .	21
Carboniferous System . .	8	Llangwm (mound) . . .	21
Carndochan Castle . .	15, 37	Llys Gwenllian (mound) . .	19
Carrog Mound . . .	21	Ludlow Series . . .	37
Cefn Rock	10	Main Rock	10
Cefn y fedw Sandstone . .	11	Millstone Grit . . .	11
Chester	1	Mold (Bailey Hill) . .	18
Coal Measures . . .	8	Old Red Sandstone . .	13
Coed yr allt Sandstone . .	10	Ordovician System . . .	14
Conway Castle . .	14, 43	Prestatyn Castle . .	13, 22
Criccieth Castle . .	15, 38	Precambrian Rocks . .	15
Crogen (mound) . . .	21	Premier Coal . . .	9
Deganwy Castle . .	15, 35	Prysor (mound) . . .	19
Denbigh Castle . .	13, 28	Purple Sandstone . .	30, 42
Dinas Bran (castle) . .	14, 36	Rhuddlan Castle . .	13, 42
Dodleston (mound) . .	17	Rhuddlan Mound . . .	17
Dolbadarn Castle . .	15, 33	Rhyolite	44
Dolwyddelan Castle . .	15, 31	Rofft Mount	18
Drift deposits . . .	6	Rug (mound)	21
Dyserth Castle . .	13, 23	Ruthin Castle . .	8, 25
Erddig Mound . . .	18	Silurian System . . .	14
Ewloe Castle . . .	11, 34	Talacre Stone . . .	11
Ewloe Castle Rock . . .	11	Tomen y Mur . . .	19
Felsite	38	Tomen y Rhodwydd . .	18
Flint Castle . .	11, 41	Tomen y Vaerdre . . .	19
Foel Las (mound) . .	21	Triassic System . . .	7
Glacial Deposits . . .	6	Ucheldre (mound) . . .	21
Gronw (mound) . . .	21	Yard Rock	11